Vocabulary Transparencies and Copymasters

McDougal Littell

THE LANGUAGE OF
LITERATURE

GRADE NINE

McDougal Littell
A HOUGHTON MIFFLIN COMPANY
Evanston, Illinois • Boston • Dallas

ISBN 0-395-96808-9

Copyright © 2000 by McDougal Littell Inc.
Box 1667, Evanston, Illinois 60204
All rights reserved. Printed in the United States of America.

1 2 3 4 5 6 7 8 9 – SJT – 02 01 00 99

Table of Contents

To the Teacher

Introduction
Each transparency in the Vocabulary Transparencies and Copymasters book provides an opportunity for students to study and apply the variety of vocabulary and word analysis skills that are essential to the understanding and the enjoyment of literature. These are skills that are valuable to students in and beyond the language arts classroom.

When to Use
The Vocabulary Transparencies and Copymasters book is a flexible teaching tool. The book provides teaching options for the vocabulary skills introduced in the Pupil's Edition and the Teacher's Edition.

Because each transparency may either be used to teach a specific concept to the entire class or be photocopied for a single student facing a stumbling block, the transparencies will meet a wide variety of student needs.

The transparencies may be used for **preteaching**—to introduce concepts before students begin an assignment; for **reference**—to provide extra help as well as to supplement the Vocabulary Mini Lessons in the Teacher's Edition and the Vocabulary SkillBuilder pages in the Unit Resource Books; and for **reteaching**—to review and reteach specific concepts that the class has struggled with while reading.

Copymasters provide additional practice using vocabulary skills taught in the grade.

Vocabulary Transparencies
The sixteen vocabulary transparencies provide instruction and model application of skills such as using context clues, connotation and denotation, and word analysis strategies to determine the meaning of unfamiliar words. The vocabulary transparencies support the instruction on the Building Vocabulary pages in the Pupil's Edition and can be used with more than one selection.

How to Use
In a darkened classroom, use an overhead projector to display a transparency on a screen or a chalkboard. You may wish to read the transparency aloud or call upon student volunteers to assist you, thereby engaging the attention and interest of the entire class.

The transparencies may also be photocopied and distributed to students. For high-quality copies, lay a blank sheet of paper over the transparency when photocopying. Students may read through the exercises independently, or with a partner or small group; they may also wish to build their own vocabulary handbooks by collecting copies of the transparencies in folders or binders for easy access and reference.

Vocabulary Copymasters

Vocabulary copymasters provide practice of the vocabulary skills and strategies taught in Vocabulary Mini Lessons in the Teacher's Edition and on the vocabulary transparencies. Each copymaster provides a summary of skill instruction and additional practice exercises in the same format as those in the Teacher's Edition Vocabulary Mini Lessons. Answers to all copymaster practice exercises are provided in an easy-to-follow Answer Key at the end of the book.

How to Use

The brief instruction at the top of each copymaster offers an opportunity to review the basic concept of the lesson. The copymasters may be used for practice as a follow-up to the Teacher's Edition Mini Lessons or as a review of vocabulary skills. Answers to all copymaster practice exercises are provided in an easy-to-follow answer key at the end of the book.

Personal Word List

Name: _____ Selection: _____

Word	Page	What I Think the Word Means	Dictionary Definition

Context Clues

Readers can sometimes understand the meaning of an unfamiliar word by examining the context in which the word is used. Consider the following sentence from "The Necklace."

> Instead of being delighted, as her husband had hoped, she <u>scornfully</u> tossed the invitation on the table, murmuring, "What good is that to me?"

From the meaning of the sentence, it can be inferred that the word *scornfully* means "contemptuously; disdainfully."

Infer Meanings   Read the following sentences. Then use context clues to determine the meaning of each underlined word from "The Necklace." On the lines below each sentence, write the meaning that you infer.

1. My sister is so <u>thrifty</u> that she keeps old brown paper bags and reuses them as wrapping paper for gifts.

   _____

   _____

2. How will Tamika deal with her <u>predicament</u>—whether to remain silent or to inform the teacher that her friend cheated on the final exam?

   _____

   _____

3. The soccer team was <u>disconsolate</u> after losing a close match and narrowly missing a chance to clinch the division title.

   _____

   _____

4. A car alarm sounded <u>incessantly</u> for half an hour until the car's owner finally arrived to turn it off.

   _____

   _____

5. Heidi's parents were <u>distressed</u> when the school nurse called to tell them that their daughter had been injured during field hockey practice.

   _____

   _____

Context Clues

Sometimes readers can understand an unfamiliar word by examining the context in which the word is used. Consider the following sentence from "The Most Dangerous Game."

> Some wounded thing, by the evidence a large animal, had <u>thrashed</u> about in the underbrush; the jungle weeds were crushed down, and the moss was lacerated; one patch of weeds was stained crimson.

From the meaning of the sentence, readers can infer that the meaning of the word *thrashed* is "moved violently or wildly."

Infer Meaning Read each of the following sentences. Use context clues to determine the meaning of the underlined word from "The Most Dangerous Game." Then circle the letter of the definition that most closely matches the word's meaning.

1. As the fog slowly lifted, the captain of the ship <u>discerned</u> land.

   a. avoided   b. perceived   c. navigated   d. approached

2. An <u>ardent</u> bowler, Mr. Wolff bowls three times a week with his friends, watches candlepin bowling on television, and collects numerous trophies in bowling tournaments.

   a. amateur   b. aggressive   c. average   d. enthusiastic

3. Divers made one last <u>futile</u> attempt to recover the sunken treasure but gave up when their search yielded nothing.

   a. useless   b. dangerous   c. illegal   d. productive

4. Ben <u>indolently</u> reclined in the shade and sipped ice water, while his younger brother mowed the entire lawn by himself.

   a. energetically   b. lazily   c. secretly   d. humbly

5. To help us find our lost dog, our <u>solicitous</u> neighbors spent an hour driving around our neighborhood hunting for him in the middle of the night.

   a. noisy   b. curious   c. thoughtful   d. thoughtless

Word Origins

The word *receding* is based upon the Latin root *cedere,* which means "to go, withdraw, yield." In "The Most Dangerous Game," Rainsford tries to swim toward the yacht's lights, which are receding or moving away from him. Other words based on the same root are *precede, proceed, access, cease,* and *ancestor.* Knowledge of the root word *cedere* can help readers remember the meanings of these words.

Find Meanings Find the meaning of each of the following words. Write the meaning on the line below each word. Then use each word in a sentence, writing it on the lines provided.

1. precede

Meaning: _____

Sentence: _____

_____

2. proceed

Meaning: _____

Sentence: _____

_____

3. access

Meaning: _____

Sentence: _____

_____

4. cease

Meaning: _____

Sentence: _____

_____

5. ancestor

Meaning: _____

Sentence: _____

_____

Antonyms

Antonyms are words that have opposite or almost opposite meanings. The meaning of an unfamiliar word in a sentence can sometimes be inferred when its antonym appears in the same sentence. Read the following sentence, for example:

> After <u>vanishing</u> from the stage for several years, the popular actress began <u>appearing</u> again on Broadway in a hit play.

Once readers determine from context that *vanishing* is an antonym for *appearing*, they can infer that *vanishing* means "disappearing, withdrawing."

Infer Meanings Read each of the following sentences. Use antonyms to infer the meaning of the underlined word from "Where Have You Gone, Charming Billy?" Then write the meaning you infer on the lines below each sentence.

1. <u>Puffy</u> cumulous clouds floated in the sky yesterday, but flat stratus clouds gathered today.

   _____

   _____

2. During the newscast, the TV anchor managed to <u>stifle</u> a laugh, but he felt that he could allow himself a smile when he read the absurd news story.

   _____

   _____

3. Although they are similar words, a composter enhances the process of <u>decay</u>, while compost provides nourishment to aid plant growth.

   _____

   _____

4. A tornado <u>skirted</u> the city but passed through the nearby suburbs.

   _____

   _____

5. The counselor had to keep track of the hikers who were walking ahead of the group as well as those who were <u>trailing</u> it.

   _____

   _____

Context Clues

Words and phrases such as *but, unlike, in contrast to,* and *although* are used to indicate contrast. For example, read the following sentence from "Marigolds."

> Her big frame still held traces of the tall, powerful woman she must have been in youth, although it was now bent and <u>drawn</u>.

The contrast clue *although* helps readers infer the meaning of *drawn.* From the context of the sentence, it is apparent that Miss Lottie had once been tall and strong but was now stooped and unhealthy-looking.

Infer Meanings Read each of the following sentences. Use context clues that indicate contrast to determine the meaning of the underlined word from "Marigolds." Then write the meaning you infer on the lines below each sentence.

1. Although most of the movie was <u>audible</u>, Juan could not hear all the dialogue and asked the projectionist to increase the volume.

_____

_____

2. My grandfather was once sluggish and inactive, but his visits to a health club have given him renewed <u>vigor</u>.

_____

_____

3. In contrast to the <u>monotonous</u> drum solo at the end of the song, the thrilling guitar riffs at the beginning are electrifying.

_____

_____

4. The lush fruitfulness of an oasis is totally unlike the <u>sterility</u> of the desert in which it is found.

_____

_____

5. Andrew felt <u>bewilderment</u> after arriving in the foreign city, but he soon learned how to get around with the aid of a map and a guide book.

_____

_____

Prefixes

Many English words are composed of word parts called **prefixes** that have been placed in front of words known as **basewords.** Knowledge of prefixes can help readers determine the meaning of unfamiliar words. For example, the word *multicolored* is made up of the prefix *multi-,* which means "many," "much," or "multiple," and the base word *colored,* which means "having color." In "Marigolds," Lizabeth compares her chaotic emotions during adolescence to a "multicolored skein," meaning that her different feelings were like a coil of many-colored yarns. The prefix *multi-* occurs in a number of other words, including *multimedia, multicultural, multidirectional, multipurpose,* and *multinational.*

Determine Meanings Use your knowledge of the prefix *multi-* to determine the meaning of each of the following words. Write down a definition of the word on the chart below. Check the accuracy of each definition in a dictionary.

Word	Meaning
1. multimedia	
2. multicultural	
3. multidirectional	
4. multipurpose	
5. multinational	

Context Clues

Sometimes readers can understand the meaning of an unfamiliar word by examining the context in which the word is used. Finding cause-and-effect relationships often helps readers determine a word's meaning. Consider the following passage from *The Perfect Storm*.

> Just as he's about to ride up, the wave hits . . . It's huge and cresting, fifty or sixty feet. It <u>avalanches</u> over Moore and buries both him and the lift basket.

A large wave hits Moore; as a result, he and the lift basket are covered with water. From the cause-and-effect relationship in this passage, readers can infer that the word *avalanches* means "inundates or overwhelms."

Infer Meanings In each of the following sentences, use the cause-and-effect relationship to help you determine the meanings of the underlined words from *The Perfect Storm*. Write the meanings you infer on the lines below each sentence.

1. The looters <u>frantically</u> fled from the police because they did not want to be arrested.

   _____

   _____

2. During a <u>lull</u> in the fighting, the platoon of soldiers relaxed and joked.

   _____

   _____

3. The driver <u>maneuvered</u> his car around the icy patch and prevented the accident.

   _____

   _____

4. After the successful peace talks were concluded, the two nations were on more <u>cordial</u> terms.

   _____

   _____

5. While playing basketball, Daniel slipped on a wet spot on the floor and <u>wrenched</u> his ankle.

   _____

   _____

Using Reference Materials

Readers can find the precise meaning of technical vocabulary by using **reference materials** such as technical books, dictionaries, and encyclopedias. For example, read the following sentence from *The Perfect Storm*.

> Occasionally the wind blows a <u>crest</u> off, and he has to dive under the cascade of <u>whitewater</u> before setting out again.

The precise meanings of technical vocabulary in the sentence—the words *crest* and *whitewater*—might be found in a book on oceans, in an encyclopedia article about sailing, or in a dictionary.

Find Precise Meanings Read the following sentences from *The Perfect Storm*. Use reference materials to find the precise meaning of each of the underlined words. Then write the meaning on the lines below each sentence.

1. The Falcon comes back at 140 knots, <u>radar</u> locked onto the helicopter.

_____

_____

2. The pilot comes screaming over the *Satori's* mast and the copilot pushes two life-raft packages out a <u>hatch</u> in the floorboards.

_____

_____

3. Two helicopters, two Falcon jets, a medium-range <u>cutter</u>, and a hundred air- and seamen have already been committed to the rescue.

_____

_____

4. He puts on socks and hood, straps on swim fins, pulls a mask and <u>snorkel</u> down over his head, and then struggles into his neoprene gloves.

_____

_____

5. The H-3 thunders overhead, <u>rotors</u> blasting a lily-pad of flattened water into the sea.

_____

_____

Connotation

Connotations are the ideas or feelings that a word may suggest which may be different from its exact dictionary definition. For example, read the following lines from "The Wreck of the Hesperus:"

> For I can <u>weather</u> the roughest gale
> That ever wind did blow.

In the context of the poem, the verb *weather* means "come through safely" or "survive." However, other meanings for *weather* include "adverse or destructive atmospheric conditions, such as high winds or heavy rain," "expose to the action of the elements," and "disintegrate or discolor." Longfellow may have used the word *weather* to suggest the adverse experience of being exposed to the harsh conditions created by a storm.

Identify Connotations Read the following words from Longfellow's poem. On the lines provided, write down the connotations that each word suggests. Then discuss with classmates why Longfellow may have chosen these words.

1. stinging

   _____

   _____

2. blast

   _____

   _____

3. lashed

   _____

   _____

4. stilled

   _____

   _____

5. rattling

   _____

   _____

Using a Dictionary to Determine Precise Meanings

A dictionary can help a reader determine the precise meanings of unfamiliar words. For example, look at the dictionary definition and origin of *illuminated,* a word from "The Gift of the Magi," listed in the chart below.

Determine Precise Meanings Use a dictionary to determine the meanings and origins of the following words from "The Gift of the Magi" and write them in the chart. When you encounter a word that has more than one meaning, use context to decide which meaning is most appropriate. An example has been provided for you.

Word	Meaning(s)	Origin
illuminated	*clarified*	*from Latin illuminare, illuminat- : in, in + luminare, to light up*
1. shabby		
2. laboriously		
3. falter		
4. subside		
5. calculated		

Antonyms

Sometimes a sentence includes a word and its **antonym,** a word with the opposite meaning. Knowing the meaning of a word's antonym can help readers infer the meaning of an unfamiliar word. For example, read the following sentence:

> When the light turned red, a pedestrian ambled across the street but then <u>darted</u> out of the way as a speeding ambulance careened around the corner.

The antonym *ambled,* meaning "walked slowly or leisurely," helps readers determine the meaning of the word *darted,* "moved suddenly and rapidly."

Identify Antonyms Read each of the following sentences. Circle the antonym that helps you determine the meaning of the underlined word. Then find and write the dictionary definition of the underlined word.

1. Don glanced at the woman but then <u>peered</u> more closely at her when he realized

   that she was a celebrity in disguise.

   Definition: _____

   _____

2. Do not be <u>reckless</u> when baby-sitting; be careful to watch the child at all times.

   Definition: _____

   _____

3. The king's soldiers quickly <u>retired</u> behind the castle walls as the enemy troops

   approached on horseback.

   Definition: _____

   _____

4. Some students have an <u>eagerness</u> to learn math, while others show indifference

   toward the subject.

   Definition: _____

   _____

5. Following the earthquake, the clerk returned to the shop to clean up the <u>shattered</u>

   vases and stained glass and to put any intact ceramic figurines back on the shelves.

   Definition: _____

   _____

Using Context to Determine Meaning

Words and phrases such as *like, in the same way, as,* and *similar* indicate comparisons. In sentences containing these terms, it is often possible to figure out the meaning of an unfamiliar word from the context of the comparison. Consider the following sentence.

> Miss Strangeworth carefully tended her <u>dainty</u> roses as if they were made of antique glass.

The meaning of the word *dainty,* "delicate," can be inferred from the comparison of the roses to fragile antique glass.

Infer Meanings Read the following sentences. Use comparison context clues to determine the meaning of each of the underlined words from "The Possibility of Evil." Write the meaning you infer on the lines below each sentence.

1. Like a person who has just won the lottery, the newly elected candidate was in a <u>chipper</u> mood.

   _____

   _____

2. Similar to two peas in a pod, an <u>infatuated</u> couple never seems to be apart.

   _____

   _____

3. The <u>luxury</u> of the island resort was like extra whipped cream on dessert.

   _____

   _____

4. Kyle became <u>unduly</u> upset when his brother made the small mistake and totally lost his temper, in the same way that a baseball coach becomes extremely angry over a bad, but unimportant, call and argues with an umpire until he is ejected from the game.

   _____

   _____

5. Observing the <u>sloppiness</u> of my room, my parents said it looked as if a tornado had passed through it.

   _____

   _____

Analogies

Questions on standardized tests often require the identification of the relationship of word pairs in analogies. In an analogy, the relationship between the two words in the first pair is the same as the relationship between the two words in the second pair. For example, study the following analogy:

FRAGRANT : STINKY : :

a. sour : tart   b. aroma : stench   c. gigantic : tiny   d. silly : tall

Fragrant and *stinky* are adjectives that have opposite meanings. The two words in the pair that best completes the analogy, *gigantic* and *tiny,* are also adjectives that are opposite in meaning.

Complete Analogies Circle the letter of the word pair that best completes each analogy below.

1. TOURIST : VISITOR : :
   a. host : guest
   b. magazine : periodical
   c. curious : inquisitive
   d. mall : salesperson

2. HONORED : RESPECTED : :
   a. hired : fired
   b. courage : cowardice
   c. possessed : inherited
   d. cherished : treasured

3. GLANCE : STARE : :
   a. smile : frown
   b. serious : grave
   c. stroll : run
   d. laugh : speak

4. ABSENTMINDED : PREOCCUPIED : :
   a. polite : courteous
   b. ignorant : educated
   c. evil : stylish
   d. intelligence : knowledge

5. SECRETLY : OPENLY : :
   a. quietly : silently
   b. conceal : hide
   c. lazily : indolent
   d. quickly : slowly

Context Clues

Sometimes an author restates a difficult word in slightly easier language. Often, commas or other punctuation marks and/or words and phrases are signals that clue readers to look for a restatement. For example, read the following sentence about Juan, a character in "The Censors":

Juan knew he would have to be keen—alert and sharp—to catch the cheats.

The difficult word in the sentence, *keen,* is restated in slightly easier language: *alert* and *sharp.* The dashes signal the restatement to the reader.

Identify Restatements Read the following sentences. In each sentence, identify and underline a word from "The Censors" that has been restated. On the lines below each sentence, write the meaning of that word. Finally, circle the punctuation marks and/or words or phrases that signal the restatement.

1. In a thrilling performance, Carlos demonstrated his zeal, his passion, for native folk dances.

   _____

   _____

2. Her negligence, that is, her carelessness in leaving her little sister alone while she went roller-blading, is appalling.

   _____

   _____

3. After the completion of a difficult project, the festive, or merry, mood in the office was obvious.

   _____

   _____

4. The postal employee decided to intercept a suspicious package; in other words, she stopped the item from being delivered.

   _____

   _____

5. A pilot's responsibility is to avoid putting passengers in jeopardy, meaning peril or danger.

   _____

   _____

Connotation

A word's **denotation** is its literal meaning, while its **connotation** refers to the subtle shades of meaning that are attached to the word. For example, find the following line from the fourth section of the poem "The Bells."

Hear the <u>tolling</u> of the bells—

Within this section of the poem, the word *tolling* means "sounding slowly" but also has associations of grief and sadness because bells are sometimes tolled to announce a person's death, a funeral, or a disaster.

Complete a Chart Find and read each of the following lines from "The Bells." On the chart below, write the denotation and a possible connotation for each underlined word.

Line	Denotation	Connotation
1. In the <u>startled</u> ear of Night		
2. Too much <u>horrified</u> to speak		
3. With a <u>desperate</u> desire		
4. What a tale their <u>terror</u> tells		
5. In the <u>clamor</u> and the clangor of the bells		

Using Reference Materials

Using a dictionary and thesaurus is often the most efficient way to define an unfamiliar word. For example, study the following reference source entries for the word *revenge:*

> **Dictionary:** <u>revenge</u> *n.* 1. the act of taking vengeance for injuries or wrongs. 2. something done in vengeance. 3. a desire for revenge; spite or vindictiveness. 4. an opportunity to retaliate

> **Thesaurus:** <u>revenge</u> *n.* vengeance, vendetta, retaliation, rancor, vindictiveness.

The dictionary lists multiple definitions beginning with the most common. The thesaurus lists synonyms, each of which may have a slightly different connotation. By combining data from both of these sources, a reader can develop literal and connotative meanings for the word *revenge.*

Find Meanings In a thesaurus, look up each of the following words from "The Cask of Amontillado." For each word, write five of the synonyms that you find. Then use two of the synonyms—each with a slightly different connotation—in sentences.

1. retribution

   Synonyms: _____

   Sentence 1: _____

   Sentence 2: _____

2. abscond

   Synonyms: _____

   Sentence 1: _____

   Sentence 2: _____

3. gait

   Synonyms: _____

   Sentence 1: _____

   Sentence 2: _____

4. jest

   Synonyms: _____

   Sentence 1: _____

   Sentence 2: _____

5. obstinate

   Synonyms: _____

   Sentence 1: _____

   Sentence 2: _____

Meanings of Roots

Sometimes readers can determine the meaning of a word by defining its root. A **root** is a base word or word part, often derived from Greek or Latin, that contains the core meaning of the word. The meaning of the word varies depending upon the affix that is used. For example, read the following sentence:

Fortunato failed to perceive the diabolical plot for <u>revenge</u> that Montresor had hatched. (vengier = to take vengence)

The word *revenge* comes from the French *vengier.* By combining the meaning of the root *venge,* "vengeance," with the prefix *re-,* meaning "again," readers can determine that a meaning for *revenge* is "to take vengeance again."

Determine Meanings Read each of the following sentences. Use the root meaning that appears in parentheses to determine a meaning for the underlined words from "The Cask of Amontillado." Write the meaning you infer on the lines provided.

1. We passed through a range of low arches, <u>descended</u>, passed on . . . (*scand* = to climb)

   _____

   _____

2. Fortunato's <u>intoxication</u> made him more vulnerable to being tricked by the devious Montresor. (*tox* = poison)

   _____

   _____

3. Being trapped in the catacombs and buried alive seemed to be an <u>insufferably</u> harsh fate for Fortunato. (*ferre* = to bear)

   _____

   _____

4. Why do you think Montresor decided to <u>impose</u> such a cruel punishment on Fortunato? (*ponere* = place, put)

   _____

   _____

5. What <u>disturbed</u> me most about Poe's story was Montresor's lack of remorse for his actions. (*turbo* = agitate)

   _____

   _____

Synonyms

Synonyms are words that have the same or nearly the same meaning. For example, read the following list of synonyms that Kingsolver uses for the everyday word *clothing* throughout her essay, "Life Without Go-Go Boots:" *apparel, outfit, raiment, uniform, hand-me-down.*

Synonyms for words are found in reference books such as the dictionary and thesaurus.

Find Synonyms Read each of the following sentences. Look up the underlined word in a dictionary or thesaurus. Using the words from "Life Without Go-Go Boots" that are listed in the box below, choose the synonym that best replaces the underlined word. Write the synonym on the line below the sentence. Remember that synonyms are the same part of speech.

stunt	irreparable	spectacle	presumed
endurable	contrived	supremely	reigned
trendy	stature	fortuitous	inclement

1. Many celebrities attended the party at the <u>fashionable</u> nightspot.

   _____

2. <u>Stormy</u> weather prevented us from sailing up the coast.

   _____

3. A wait of only fifteen minutes to get a seat in that popular restaurant seems <u>tolerable</u>.

   _____

4. Most professional basketball players have a <u>height</u> of well over six feet.

   _____

5. The store's security guard <u>devised</u> a clever plan to catch shoplifters.

   _____

Context Clues

When a reader encounters a new word, he or she often uses clues in the sentence to figure out its meaning. Consider the clues in the following sentence that help to define *revenge.*

> He hears the shot and escapes but when he learns at dawn how Bess died he goes into a rage and returns for <u>revenge</u> . . .

The main clues are the words "goes into a rage and returns." Readers can infer that *revenge* means "an act of inflicting injury in order to get even."

Define Unfamiliar Words Use clues in each sentence below to help you figure out the meaning of the underlined word. After you write your own definition, look up the word in a dictionary. Write the dictionary definition after yours.

1. The gloomy, drafty hospital was a <u>dismal</u> place in which to spend two weeks.

   Your definition: _____

   Dictionary definition: _____

2. It seemed to Frank that the overworked nurses were often scowling and <u>grimacing</u> at him when he called for them during the night.

   Your definition: _____

   Dictionary definition: _____

3. Seamus was delighted to listen as young Frank <u>deftly</u> read aloud the beautifully written words of William Shakespeare.

   Your definition: _____

   Dictionary definition: _____

4. Even though Frank was very hungry, he was <u>finicky</u> about eating the grayish, lukewarm food that the hospital provided.

   Your definition: _____

   Dictionary definition: _____

5. Seamus says Patricia is a lovely girl because she often gives him sweets from the <u>parcel</u> her mother sends every fortnight.

   Your definition: _____

   Dictionary definition: _____

Dialect

Context clues can help readers with more than just unfamiliar words. They can also help readers understand words that are unique to a specific dialect.

Investigate Irish Dialect Each of the following sentences from *Angela's Ashes* uses some Irish dialect. Use the context of the sentence to determine the meaning of the underlined word. Rewrite the sentence in your own words, then write the meaning of the underlined word.

1. Sister Rita said one more word out of him and upstairs with him. We gave ye a warning to stop the <u>blathering</u>, but ye wouldn't.

   Rewrite: _____

   _____

   Meaning of word: _____

2. Seamus says <u>'twas</u> a terrible thing indeed . . .

   Rewrite: _____

   _____

   Meaning of word: _____

3. She said <u>'twould</u> break your heart to think of what the English did to us . . .

   Rewrite: _____

   _____

   Meaning of word: _____

4. Mam is sitting by the bed and the nurse is saying, You know, <u>missus</u>, this is very unusual.

   Rewrite: _____

   _____

   Meaning of word: _____

5. Take the <u>by</u>, Seamus, take him.

   Rewrite: _____

   _____

   Meaning of word: _____

Antonyms

An **antonym** is a word that means the opposite of another word. Sometimes a reader comes across an unfamiliar word but is familiar with an antonym of the word that appears nearby in the text. If the context makes it clear that the two words are antonyms, the reader can figure out the meaning of the unfamiliar word.

Use Antonyms In each excerpt from "Unfinished Business," a word that may be unfamiliar to you is used, along with a nearby antonym. Use your understanding of the italicized antonym to infer the meaning of the underlined word. Then write a definition of the underlined word on the lines provided.

1. And the father couldn't <u>communicate</u> with her. He was a very *nonverbal* man.

   Definition: _____

   _____

2. My work is <u>preventive</u> psychiatry, it's to finish as much as possible before death, like we bring flowers to our patients before they die so we don't have to pile them up on the casket *afterward.*

   Definition: _____

   _____

3. If you don't mind, I'm going to ask her <u>straightforward</u>, not in *symbolic* language, why she can't die, if that's O.K. with you.

   Definition: _____

   _____

4. Hanging on to him, she started to sob and sob and cry, not *painful* crying but tremendous <u>relief</u>.

   Definition: _____

   _____

5. "And I want you to come in and see how I'm doing so you're never *worried* that I'm hurting anybody." She had great <u>faith</u> in me.

   Definition: _____

   _____

Using a Dictionary

A **dictionary** gives the meaning and pronunciation of a word as well as information about its origins and history. Readers can use a dictionary to help them determine the precise meanings of words.

Locate Definitions Use a dictionary to find a precise meaning for each of the words listed in section A. Write the definition beside each word. Then choose an appropriate word to complete each sentence in section B.

A.

1. acquaintance _____

2. armada _____

3. bantam _____

4. dilapidated _____

5. enterprise _____

6. glower _____

7. inhabit _____

8. mingle _____

9. rummage _____

10. tabulate _____

B.

11. I _____ a large home with my parents and siblings.

12. At the end of your shift, you must _____ all the shoes you sold by style and size.

13. The old, _____ house had broken windows, peeling paint, and loose shutters.

14. Ferdinand is much more than an _____; we've been friends for over six years.

15. Please don't _____ through the garbage looking for jewels—there is nothing of value in there.

Idioms

An **idiom** is an expression that has a meaning that is different from the literal meaning of its individual words. Frequently, the meaning of an idiom can be determined from its context. Notice the underlined words in the following sentence.

> My mother reminded us that we had to clear the sink and leave enough counter space to <u>dress the turkey</u> before putting it in the oven.

In this sentence, the phrases "clear the sink and leave enough counter space" and "before putting it in the oven" help you infer that *dressing the turkey* must mean cleaning it, putting stuffing inside it, and tying it up to roast it.

Determine the Meaning of Idioms Read each of the following sentences. Then use context clues to determine the meaning of the underlined idiom. Write the meaning on the lines that follow each sentence.

1. Buddy's cousin asked him to <u>keep an eye on</u> the pot that was simmering on the stove.

   Meaning of idiom: _____

   _____

2. Mr. Haha thought that Buddy and his cousin were <u>putting him on</u> when they said that they needed whiskey for their fruitcakes.

   Meaning of idiom: _____

   _____

3. For Buddy, the details of the friction between his elderly cousins were <u>over his head</u>.

   Meaning of idiom: _____

   _____

4. Compared to the amount of money that they needed, the small change contributed by their cousins was only <u>a drop in the bucket</u>.

   Meaning of idiom: _____

   _____

5. Buddy and his cousin <u>explored every avenue</u> to gather enough money to purchase the ingredients necessary for the fruitcakes.

   Meaning of idiom: _____

   _____

Context Clues

One way to figure out the meaning of an unfamiliar word is to look for context clues. The following sentence has a cause-and-effect context clue that helps define the word *coordinate*.

> Since the players <u>coordinate</u> their offensive and defensive efforts, they do quite well in their division.

The "cause" is that the players coordinate their efforts; the "effect" is that they do well in their division. A reader can infer that *coordinate* means "put in order or put together."

Use Cause-and-Effect Clues In each sentence that follows, underline the cause with a single line. Underline the effect with a double line. Then use your understanding of the cause-and-effect relationship to define the italicized word.

1. When we *anticipate* danger and behave cautiously, we can sometimes avoid problems altogether.

   Definition: _____

   _____

2. Because we were new to the community, I *endured* a long and lonely summer.

   Definition: _____

   _____

3. As a consequence of Mike's *phenomenal* catch, he became captain of the team.

   Definition: _____

   _____

4. Rosa became very *agitated* when no one answered the telephone when she called home during the storm.

   Definition: _____

   _____

5. The committee chairperson was not *enthralled* with our idea, so we had to come up with a new plan.

   Definition: _____

   _____

Context Clues

The context in which a word is used can provide clues about its meaning. Readers can sometimes make inferences about a word's meaning based on other words or phrases in the same sentence. Try to figure out the meaning of the word *hoax* in the following sentence.

That was quite a <u>hoax</u> you put on, making your sister believe she had seen a ghost.

The phrases "you put on" and "making your sister believe" are context clues that can help you infer that a *hoax* means "a trick."

Infer the Meanings of Words Use context clues to figure out the meaning of the underlined word in each of the sentences below. Then write the word's meaning on the lines provided.

1. The characters in that novel are <u>static</u>, or unchanging.

   Definition: _____

   _____

2. <u>Trembling</u> at the thought of meeting her enemy again, Maria's teeth chattered, her knees knocked, and a chill ran up her spine.

   Definition: _____

   _____

3. The rain <u>erodes</u> the soil on the beach, so that after several years there is noticeably less sand.

   Definition: _____

   _____

4. It is so <u>humid</u> outside that it almost feels as if the air is misting your face.

   Definition: _____

   _____

5. Let's make <u>tentative</u> plans for Friday, and then hope that nothing comes up to force us to reschedule.

   Definition: _____

   _____

Word Origins

Sometimes interesting facts about a word's origin can help a reader to remember its meaning. To discover a word's meaning, research it in a dictionary that provides information about word origins. Languages that have contributed words to modern English include Greek, Latin, Old English, and Middle English.

Investigate Word Origins Write a definition for each word listed in the chart shown below, then identify its origin. Use a dictionary to help you.

Word	Definition	Origin
1. poise		
2. surmise		
3. accumulate		
4. vagary		
5. aberration		
6. bucolic		
7. deleterious		
8. gossamer		
9. naive		
10. regale		

Context Clues

Sometimes readers can figure out the meaning of an unfamiliar word in a sentence through example clues that are provided within that sentence or a nearby one. The following sentences from "Brothers Are the Same" provide example clues that can help readers understand the meaning of the word *armament.*

> He used them now to glance at his weapons, which lay beside him—a spear, a rawhide shield. These, and a short sword at his belt, were his <u>armament</u>.

The words *spear, shield,* and *sword* are example clues that can help readers understand that *armament* means "weaponry."

Use Example Clues to Determine Meaning Read the sentences below. In each sentence, identify the example clue that helps you understand the meaning of the underlined word. Then, in the chart that follows the sentences, record the example clue and the meaning of the word as you infer from context.

1. He had <u>confronted</u> the lion with great courage, namely by rushing at it with his spear pointed at the great beast's chest.

2. The wait for help seemed <u>interminable</u>, especially the long hours until his partner returned.

3. The young warrior's <u>vanity</u> was apparent in his proud stance and his boldly decorated attire.

4. The leader showed his <u>contempt</u> with a scornful curl of his lip and a dismissive shrug of his shoulders.

5. In his victory, he received many <u>accolades</u>, including crisp salutes, applause, and eventually a medal.

Word	Example Clue	Word Meaning
1. confronted		
2. interminable		
3. vanity		
4. contempt		
5. accolades		

Antonyms

An **antonym**—a word with an opposite or nearly opposite meaning—can sometimes help readers figure out the meaning of an unfamiliar word. In the sentence below, try to infer the meaning of the word *mirth* from its antonym or antonyms.

The sound of his voice held no <u>mirth</u>; instead, it was full of sadness and despair.

From the meaning of the sentence, you can infer that *sadness* and *despair* are both antonyms for *mirth*, which means "glee, delight."

Identify Antonyms Read each of the following sentences. Find the antonym for the underlined word and circle it. Then write a definition of the underlined word based on your understanding of its antonym.

1. Although Jon was sure-footed when he set off on the hike, he began to <u>falter</u> as the trail became steep and rocky.

   Definition: _____

   _____

2. Considering his longterm <u>affinity</u> for hiking, it was surprising how quickly Jon's dislike for the activity began to build.

   Definition: _____

   _____

3. Suddenly, Jon realized that he was <u>ravenous</u> despite the fact that he had gorged himself at breakfast.

   Definition: _____

   _____

4. Although he felt <u>inept</u>, Jon offloaded his backpack and located a snack in a quick and competent way.

   Definition: _____

   _____

5. It was extremely <u>felicitous</u> that Jon glimpsed the mountain peak just as he was thinking that this hike was totally unsuitable for him.

   Definition: _____

   _____

Prefixes and Suffixes

Sometimes it is possible to understand the meaning of a word by examining its parts, including it's roots or base words, prefixes, and suffixes. A **prefix** is a word part added to the front of a root or base word, while a **suffix** is a word part added to the end of a root or base word.

The word *refresh,* for example, is formed by the addition of the prefix *re-* to the word *fresh.* The prefix *re-* comes from the Latin word *re-* or *red-* and means "again" or "backward." When thirsty people want to refresh themselves by drinking water they wish to feel fresh again. The word *freshen* is formed by the addition of the suffix *-en* to the word *fresh.* The suffix *-en* means "become." When people want to freshen their soft drinks with more ice, they want their beverages to become fresh.

Explore Prefixes and Suffixes In a dictionary, look up each prefix and suffix listed on the chart below. Write the meaning of each in the second column. Then write at least two words that include the prefix or suffix in the third column.

Prefix	Meaning	Words
1. *dis-*		
2. *com-*		
3. *in-*		
4. *un-*		

Suffix	Meaning	Words
5. *-ful*		
6. *-less*		
7. *-hood*		
8. *-ive*		
9. *-ize*		
10. *-ist*		

Analogies

An **analogy** is a statement that compares two pairs of words. The relationship between the first pair of words is the same as the relationship between the second pair of words. In the example below, *nail* is a part of *toe*. Therefore, the word that best completes the analogy with *trunk* should have the same relationship—part to whole.

NAIL : TOE : : trunk : _____

a. storage   b. tree   c. forest

Tree best completes the analogy because it has the same relationship to *trunk* as *nail* does to *toe;* each pair shows a part-to-whole relationship—the first term in the analogy being a part of the second term. Some other types of analogies are synonyms, antonyms, and cause to effect.

Complete Analogies Determine the relationship between the first pair of words in each analogy below. Then look for the same relationship to complete the second pair. Circle the word that best completes the analogy. Then indicate in the space below each analogy what kind of relationship the analogy expresses.

1. BOLD : DARING : : comical : _____

a. grave   b. funny   c. smiling

Relationship expressed: _____

2. DANGER : FEAR : : success : _____

a. victory   b. conclusion   c. happiness

Relationship expressed: _____

3. SLICE : LOAF : : page : _____

a. book   b. tree   c. type

Relationship expressed: _____

4. THRIFT : EXTRAVAGANCE : : kindness : _____

a. tolerance   b. cruelty   c. carelessness

Relationship expressed: _____

5. MIMIC : COPY : : persuade : _____

a. convince   b. prevent   c. flatter

Relationship expressed: _____

Context Clues

A reader can often figure out the meaning of an unfamiliar word by examining the context in which the word appears. Examine the following sentence from Stephen Vincent Benét's *The Devil and Daniel Webster* in order to determine the meaning of the underlined word.

> You cannot help Mr. Stone—since you are his wife, your testimony would be prejudiced.

A reader could use the meaning of the sentence to infer the meaning of the word *prejudiced*. Because Mrs. Stone would probably testify in favor of her husband, the reader might guess that *prejudiced* means "biased."

Use Context Clues Use the context clues to determine the meaning of the underlined word in each sentence below. Write the meaning of the word.

1. In *The Devil and Daniel Webster,* the Devil pretends to be a Boston lawyer and feigns embarrassment when he is asked to play the fiddle.

_____

_____

2. The crowd is alarmed and frightened by the ominous sound of the church bell.

_____

_____

3. The Devil presents the deed that Jabez Stone has signed as incontestable evidence that Stone has sold his soul.

_____

_____

4. Webster is determined that the Devil will not prevail over the human whom the Devil threatens.

_____

_____

5. He makes a speech in support of liberty and against all oppressors.

_____

_____

Context Clues

An **idiom** is an expression that has a meaning different from the exact meaning of its individual words. People often use idioms in everyday conversation. Stephen Vincent Benét includes many in the dialogue of *The Devil and Daniel Webster.* Some of the expressions in the play are still current, while others are no longer used. When trying to figure out the meaning of an unfamiliar idiom, always examine the context in which it appears. Use context clues to determine the meaning of the underlined idiom in this sentence from *The Devil and Daniel Webster.*

> There's no need <u>to make hay and oats</u> of a trifling matter when we're both sensible men.

The speaker thinks that the matter is "trifling," or unimportant. *To make hay and oats* is the opposite of "trifling" and must mean "to spend a lot of time planning and discussing."

Use Context Clues to Understand Idioms Use the context clues to determine the meaning of each underlined idiom. Then write the meaning of the idiom.

1. Every New Year's Day, people vow <u>to turn over a new leaf</u>, hoping to bring about radical changes in their lives.

   _____

2. Dinosaurs vanished suddenly from the face of the earth, and scientists are still debating what <u>wiped them out</u>.

   _____

3. The doctor said that the patient will feel much better when the pain <u>wears off</u>.

   _____

4. You're exaggerating the importance of the situation—stop <u>making a mountain out of a molehill</u>.

   _____

5. These good times may not last, so let's <u>make hay while the sun shines</u>.

   _____

6. I think we should <u>go over</u> this equation until you understand it completely.

   _____

7. War <u>broke out</u> in August, 1914.

   _____

Using Context to Determine Meaning

Readers can sometimes determine the meaning of an unfamiliar word by examining the context and supporting details of the paragraph in which the word is used. Notice how supporting details help the reader infer the meaning of the word *discords* in this excerpt from Dr. Martin Luther King, Jr.'s "I Have a Dream" speech.

> With this faith we will be able to hew out of the mountain of despair a stone of hope. With this faith we will be able to transform the jangling <u>discords</u> of our nation into a beautiful symphony of brotherhood.

A reader could use the supporting details in these sentences to infer the meaning of the word *discords*. The first sentence introduces a contrast between the present and the past. In the second sentence, the contrast between the "jangling discords" of the present and the "beautiful symphony" of the future might lead the reader to infer that *discords* means "conflicts."

Use Details to Infer Meaning Use supporting details in each excerpt from "I Have a Dream" or "Glory and Hope" to determine the meaning of the underlined word. Write the meaning of the word.

1. This momentous decree came as a great beacon light of hope to millions of Negro slaves who had been <u>seared</u> in the flames of withering injustice.

_____

2. We must forever conduct our struggle on the high plain of dignity and discipline. We must not allow our creative protests to <u>degenerate</u> into physical violence.

_____

3. For many of our white brothers, as evidenced by their presence here today, have come to realize that their destiny is tied up with our destiny. And they have come to realize that their freedom is <u>inextricably</u> bound to our freedom.

_____

4. Your majesties, your royal highnesses, distinguished guests, comrades and friends: Today, all of us do, by our presence here, and by our celebrations in other parts of our country and the world, <u>confer</u> glory and hope to newborn liberty.

_____

5. As a token of its commitment to the renewal of our country, the new Interim Government of National Unity will, as a matter of urgency, address the issue of <u>amnesty</u> for various categories of our people who are currently serving terms of imprisonment.

_____

Word Origins

Many English words contain roots that come from older languages, such as Greek and Latin. Understanding the meaning of roots can help a reader unlock the meaning of many unfamiliar words. Notice the underlined word in this excerpt from Martin Luther King, Jr.'s, "I Have a Dream" speech.

> . . . we cannot be satisfied as long as the Negro's basic <u>mobility</u> is from a smaller ghetto to a larger one . . .

The word *mobility* means "an ability to move," and is derived from the Latin word *movere*, which means "to move." The English words *mobile, immobile, mobilize,* and *automobile* all contain the Latin root *movere* and are all related to the idea of movement. Words that contain the same root word are said to belong to the same word family.

Research Word Origins Consult a dictionary to look up and write the definition and root of each word listed below.

1. militancy

   Definition: _____

   Root: _____

2. brutality

   Definition: _____

   Root: _____

3. prodigious

   Definition: _____

   Root: _____

4. sustain

   Definition: _____

   Root: _____

5. exhilaration

   Definition: _____

   Root: _____

Using a Dictionary

Although context clues may help a reader guess the meaning of an unfamiliar word, looking the word up in the dictionary is the best way of determining the word's precise meaning. How would one determine the meaning of the word *fanatic* in the following excerpt from "The United States vs. Susan B. Anthony" by Margaret Truman?

> On top of that drawback, she was a <u>fanatic</u>. She joined the woman's suffrage movement in 1852, when she was thirty-two years old. From then until her death in 1906, she could think of little else.

Although the context might suggest that a *fanatic* is someone obsessed with something, only a dictionary could provide the precise definition: "a person possessed by an excessive and irrational zeal, especially for a religious or political cause."

Determine Meaning Use a dictionary to look up the meaning of each word listed in the box below. Then complete each sentence with one of these words.

fortitude	futile	oratory	adamant	prestigious

1. The Upmans couldn't wait to move into their _____ new address.

2. The generation that grew up during the Depression and fought in World War II will always be remembered for its _____ .

3. With the castle surrounded by a superior military force, the defenders realized that resistance was _____ .

4. Many 19th-century politicians were great public speakers and were famous for their _____ .

5. Despite the efforts of the authorities to silence her, Susan B. Anthony remained _____ about her constitutional rights.

Using Context to Determine Meaning

English has many specialized vocabularies; people who work in law, medicine, and other scientific disciplines use technical terminology that can be difficult to understand. When coming across an unfamiliar technical term or phrase, try to guess its meaning with the help of context clues. Notice how context clues help explain the meaning of *abridge* in this passage from the Fourteenth Amendment to the U.S. Constitution, excerpted in "The United States vs. Susan B. Anthony."

> No state shall make or enforce any law which shall abridge the privileges or immunities of citizens of the United States, nor shall any state deprive any person of life, liberty, or property without due process of law. . . .

The passage explains that the rights and privileges of United States citizens cannot be affected by state laws. From the context clues, a reader would be able to determine that *abridge* means "cut short."

Determine Meaning Use context clues to determine the meaning of each underlined term. Then write the definition of the term.

1. The judge allowed Susan to walk out of the courtroom without imposing a prison sentence <u>in lieu</u> of her unpaid fine; it seemed she would pay no fine.

   _____

2. After her arrest, Susan B. Anthony was supposed to be held in <u>custody</u> until her trial. The fact that she would be held under guard interfered with her travel plans.

   _____

3. A U.S. Marshal appeared at her door with a <u>warrant</u>, authorizing him to make an arrest.

   _____

4. During the trial, District Attorney Crowley represented the government and opened the arguments for the <u>prosecution</u>.

   _____

5. Susan B. Anthony insisted that the trial was unfair—she claimed that even if she had been given a fair trial, it would not have been by her <u>peers</u>. Jury, judges, and lawyers were not her equals, but her superiors, because they could vote and she could not.

   _____

Figurative Language

Figurative language is language that expresses ideas through descriptions that are not meant to be taken literally. Simile, metaphor, and personification are all types of figurative language. In **personification,** the writer attributes human qualities to an object, animal, or idea. A **metaphor** is a comparison between two things in which one thing is said to be the other thing. A **simile** is a comparison between two things using *like* or *as*. A reader can use figurative language as a kind of context clue to determine the meaning of an unfamiliar word. In the poem "The Writer" by Richard Wilbur, a house is compared to a ship, in a simile that might help the reader guess the meaning of *gunwale* in the lines that follow.

> . . . a commotion of typewriter-keys
> Like a chain hauled over a <u>gunwale</u>

If the reader did not know the meaning of *gunwale*, the image of a chain hauled over the side of a ship might provide the clue that *gunwale* means "the upper edge of the side of a ship."

Use Figurative Language to Determine Meaning Use the figurative language in each example to determine the meaning of each underlined word. Then write the definition of the word.

1. The front of the house was like the <u>prow</u> of a ship.

   _____

2. He was as <u>obstinate</u> as a mule.

   _____

3. His face was as <u>pallid</u> as an invalid's.

   _____

4. The <u>dissonance</u> was harsh and disagreeable, like the sound of a radio broadcasting two different stations.

   _____

5. The barbarian migration turned into a <u>deluge</u>, a flood of people that overwhelmed the empire.

   _____

Analogies

An **analogy** is a statement that compares two pairs of words. The relationship between the first set of words in an analogy is the same as the relationship between the second set of words. There are different kinds of analogies. Two common kinds are antonyms—words with opposite meanings—and synonyms—words with the same meaning. The following example is an antonym analogy.

> RESIST : SUCCUMB : : admit : deny

The analogy is read as "resist *is to* succumb *as* admit *is to* deny." In this analogy, *succumb* is an antonym for *resist* just as *deny* is an antonym for *admit*.

Complete Analogies On the line preceding each analogy, write *S* or *A* to identify whether the relationship is one of synonyms or antonyms. Then, write the word from the box below that best completes each analogy.

comprehensible	treacherous	insurrection	incivility	escalate
discord	snare	chaos	frailty	incision

1. _____ POVERTY : WEALTH : : order : _____

2. _____ DEFEAT : VICTORY : : harmony : _____

3. _____ FURY : ANGER : : trap : _____

4. _____ HOPE : DESPAIR : : strength : _____

5. _____ GRIEVE : MOURN : : increase : _____

6. _____ MARVEL : WONDER : : rebellion : _____

7. _____ INNOCENT : GUILTY : : mysterious : _____

8. _____ MERCHANDISE : GOODS : : disrespect : _____

9. _____ MIRAGE : ILLUSION : : cut : _____

10. _____ THRIFTY : EXTRAVAGANT : : loyal : _____

Context Clues

Many words have multiple meanings. When coming across a familiar word used in an unfamiliar way, check for context clues that may suggest the intended meaning of the word. Notice how context clues help the reader determine the meaning of *seasoned* in the following sentence from Jack London's "To Build a Fire."

> On top, tangled in the underbrush about the trunks of several small spruce trees, was a high-water deposit of dry firewood—sticks and twigs, principally, but also larger portions of <u>seasoned</u> branches and fine, dry, last year's grasses.

The sentence lists several kinds of dry firewood—sticks and twigs, seasoned branches, and dry grasses. From this clue, the reader could figure out that *seasoned* in this context means "dried."

Find Meaning Use context clues to identify the precise meaning of each underlined word below. Write the meaning on line provided.

1. It was time for my <u>watch</u>; reluctantly, I put on my coat and changed places with the guard on duty.

   _____

2. The secret agent <u>shadowed</u> the senator day and night, observing his every move.

   _____

3. Polls and surveys analyze the <u>pulse</u> of the electorate.

   _____

4. During the Middle Ages, churches and monasteries <u>ministered</u> to the sick and homeless.

   _____

5. As soon as the general received the new <u>intelligence</u>, he ordered the troops to advance.

   _____

Prefixes

Prefixes are word parts that can be added to base words or roots in order to form new words. Look for a word with a prefix in the following sentence from Jack London's "To Build a Fire."

> Once he slowed down to a walk, but the thought of the freezing extending itself made him run again.

The word *extending* is formed from the Latin prefix *ex-*, meaning "out," and the Latin root word *tendere*, meaning "to stretch." Thus, *extending* means "stretching out." Other words that contain the same prefix are *exhale* (to breath *out*), *exhume* (to remove *out* of a grave) and *exclaim* (to call *out*). Understanding the meaning of prefixes can help a reader unlock the meanings of many unfamiliar words.

Analyze Prefixes Use a dictionary to look up each word below. Write the meaning of the word. Then write the prefix and its meaning.

1. intervene

   Word meaning: _____

   Prefix and meaning: _____

2. perimeter

   Word meaning: _____

   Prefix and meaning: _____

3. transmit

   Word meaning: _____

   Prefix and meaning: _____

4. atypical

   Word meaning: _____

   Prefix and meaning: _____

5. antecedent

   Word meaning: _____

   Prefix and meaning: _____

Context Clues

Many English words have more than one meaning. A word like *banner*, for example, can mean (1) a piece of cloth, (2) a flag, or (3) a headline. A reader should always check the context to see which meaning of a word is intended. Which meaning of the word *banner* is being used in this sentence from Jon Krakauer's "Into Thin Air"?

> In my backpack was a <u>banner</u> from *Outside* magazine, a small pennant emblazoned with a whimsical lizard that Linda, my wife, had sewn, and some other mementos with which I'd intended to pose for a series of triumphant photos.

At first glance, the word *banner* seems to mean "a headline"—after all, it has come from a magazine. However, as the writer is hoping to pose with this item for photographs on the top of a mountain, one can conclude that Krakauer intended *banner* to mean "a flag." When a word has multiple meanings, the right definition can be inferred from the context of the sentence.

Determine Meaning Use context clues to identify the precise meaning of each underlined word below. Then write the meaning on the lines provided.

1. The troops were dispatched to the new <u>theater</u> of war.

_____

_____

2. This outfit is quite <u>repellent</u>—how could anyone wear such a disgusting thing!

_____

_____

3. James has just finished writing a <u>profile</u> of the poet W. H. Auden, covering his education and career.

_____

_____

4. The director of the news show assembled a <u>panel</u> to discuss the issue.

_____

_____

5. A political party is in trouble when a <u>fringe</u> group takes control and loses touch with the majority.

_____

_____

Using a Dictionary to Determine Precise Meanings

When the meaning of a word is not clear from its context, readers should look the word up in a dictionary. Not all words, however, have individual entries. Adverbs are listed after the corresponding adjective; for example, the adverb *compulsively* would be found after the definition of the adjective *compulsive*. When words have more than one definition, readers must examine the context of the sentence to determine which meaning of the word is being used. Look at the word *negotiating* in the following sentence from "Into Thin Air" by Jon Krakauer.

> Negotiating the puzzling, infirm terrain demanded unceasing concentration, an all-but-impossible feat . . .

In the dictionary, the entry for *negotiate* presents three meanings of the word: 1. to arrange or settle by conferring or discussing, 2. to transfer title to or ownership of . . . , 3. to succeed in passing over. In the sentence above, the third meaning of *negotiate*— "to succeed in passing over"—is being used.

Identify Meaning Look up each underlined word below in a dictionary. Then use context clues to identify the appropriate meaning of the word. Write the meaning on the line provided.

1. In many parts of the world, wealth is <u>concentrated</u> in the hands of a tiny proportion of the population.

   _____

2. Diego has never been robust; he has always had a weak <u>constitution</u>.

   _____

3. We were expecting to receive a sum in the <u>neighborhood</u> of forty thousand dollars.

   _____

4. Queen Anne was very <u>partial</u> to Sarah Churchill, favoring her more than anyone else.

   _____

5. I took the <u>negatives</u> in to be developed last week.

   _____

Context Clues

When coming across an unfamiliar word, always look for context clues to determine the word's meaning. How could a reader figure out the meaning of the word *fabricated* in this sentence from "My Wonder Horse" by Sabine R. Ulibarrí?

> He was a legend. The stories told of the Wonder Horse were endless. Some true, others <u>fabricated</u>.

From the contrast between the words *true* and *fabricated,* a reader could infer that *fabricated* means "false."

Use Context Clues Use context clues to identify the precise meaning of each underlined word below. Then write the meaning of the word on the line provided.

1. The precise sensory details and figurative language in the poem <u>evoked</u> many images.

_____

_____

2. In a few short years she transformed herself from an obscure journalist to an <u>illustrious</u> novelist, famous throughout the world.

_____

_____

3. Conquering kingdom after kingdom, Alexander the Great believed he was <u>invincible</u>.

_____

_____

4. Almost everyone has suffered the <u>indignity</u> of falling down in front of other people.

_____

_____

5. The day slowly <u>waned</u> as the sky grew darker and darker.

_____

_____

Synonyms

Synonyms are words that have the same or similar meanings. No two words are exactly alike; in addition to the dictionary definition of a word, many words have distinct emotional associations, called **connotations.** In addition to providing the definition of a word, a dictionary will sometimes provide a list of synonyms, noting the connotation of each. Look at the underlined word in this sentence from "My Wonder Horse" by Sabine R. Ulibarrí. Then read the synonyms for the word that appear in the dictionary.

Listless and drowsy in the <u>lethargy</u> of late afternoon, I was dozing on my horse.

lethargy **Syn:** *lethargy, lassitude, sluggishness, torpor, stupor, languor.* These nouns refer to conditions in which a person is unable or disinclined to be active, physically or mentally. *Lethargy* often implies the operation of physically disabling factors, such as illness or overwork, or it can reflect apathy or indifference. . . . *Torpor* suggests the suspension of physical and mental activity characteristic of an animal in hibernation. . . . *Languor* is lack of vigor or spirit characteristic of one who is indolent or satiated by overindulgence in luxury or pleasure.

From this list of synonyms, it is clear that *lethargy* is the word that best fits the meaning of the sentence.

Choose the Right Synonym Use a dictionary to look up each set of synonyms below. Then choose the word from each set that best completes the sentence.

1. (limited; restricted; circumscribed)

   He was immediately placed under house arrest; his activities were

   _____ to the mansion and its grounds.

2. (outlived; outlasted)

   Many ancient Roman roads have _____ the people who

   built them by 2,000 years.

3. (mishap; misadventure; misfortune)

   After a long period of _____, her prospects began to improve.

4. (inciting; stimulating; stirring)

   They were accused of _____ a riot.

5. (mars; wounds; impairs)

   Smoking _____ one's health.

Context Clues

Readers can often use context clues to figure out the meaning of an unfamiliar word. Sometimes a context clue is an **antonym,** or a word that has the opposite meaning from the unfamiliar word.

Although Mr. Borden was <u>miserly</u>, his wife was extremely generous.

The use of the word *although* suggests that generous is the opposite of *miserly*. The dictionary meaning of *miserly* confirms that it means "in a stingy manner."

Use Antonyms as Context Clues Circle antonym context clues in each sentence that help you figure out the meaning of the underlined word. Write the meaning on the line.

1. She thought her illness was <u>chronic</u>, but it turned out to be only a temporary problem.

   Definition: _____

2. The land was left <u>fallow</u> for many years, but now it is very productive.

   Definition: _____

3. The travelers were <u>exasperated</u> by the delay, but they tried to remain patient.

   Definition: _____

4. The angry boy <u>shrieked</u> in the crowded store, while the other children talked quietly.

   Definition: _____

5. Some of the wires were easy to remove; others had to be <u>wrenched</u> from the wall.

   Definition: _____

6. Some visitors <u>lingered</u> in the park on the warm summer day, while others left quickly.

   Definition: _____

7. The balloon rose in the air and then quickly <u>descended</u> back to earth.

   Definition: _____

8. The costumes at the ball were either very <u>extravagant</u> or very simple.

   Definition: _____

Figurative Language

Figurative language is used by writers to create vivid impressions and images in readers' minds. Sometimes, figurative language is used to compare different things. By using context clues in the sentence or selection, readers can determine what the figurative language means. In the sentence below, the dress material is being compared to rough sandpaper.

The <u>dress material</u> felt <u>as rough as sandpaper</u> against the girl's arm.

Use Context Clues to Understand Figurative Language Each sentence below contains an example of figurative language. On the line that follows each sentence, identify the two things that are being compared.

1. When he fell, I grabbed him in my arms and hugged him, our laughter pealing through the swamp like a ringing bell.

   _____

2. Keeping a secret is a Herculean task, almost like holding your breath.

   _____

3. Success shimmered in the distance, gleaming like a pot of gold in the sun.

   _____

4. Promise hovered about us like leaves on a tree.

   _____

5. The cold winter air felt as dry as a bone.

   _____

6. We gazed at the full moon, which hung like a shining silver plate against the sky.

   _____

7. The broken doll lay on the ground like a fallen vase of flowers.

   _____

8. The leaf spiraled from the branch like a runaway kite.

   _____

9. When the wind died, the rain fell straight down like ropes hanging from the sky.

   _____

Denotation and Connotation

A word's **denotation** is its literal or dictionary meaning. Its **connotation** refers to the attitude or emotions that are associated with the word. Study the two sentences below:

The boy <u>walked</u> through the house.

The boy <u>crept</u> through the house.

Both words mean "to move forward," but *crept* evokes a more mysterious feeling than *walked*.

Understand Connotations and Denotations Use a thesaurus to find a synonym for the underlined word in the first sentence of each exercise below. Write the synonym on the blank line in the second sentence. Then write a short description of how the connotations of the synonym are different from those of the underlined word.

1. The critics hated the play and called it the "biggest <u>flop</u> of the year."

   The critics hated the play and called it the "biggest _____ of the year."

   _____

2. The little boy was a real <u>scamp</u> who was always getting into trouble.

   The little boy was a real _____ who was always getting into trouble.

   _____

3. The plan to build the sports center ran into a <u>snag</u> when the mayor did not approve it.

   The plan to build the sports center ran into a _____ when the mayor did not approve it.

   _____

4. Because it was such a <u>nice</u> day, the children spent it playing in the park.

   Because it was such a _____ day, the children spent it playing in the park.

   _____

5. The dancers <u>swirled</u> around the stage so quickly, the audience gasped in wonder.

   The dancers _____ around the stage so quickly, the audience gasped in wonder.

   _____

Synonyms

Synonyms are words that have the same or nearly the same meanings. Using synonym context clues can often help readers to figure out the meaning of an unfamiliar word.

The <u>transparent</u> quality of the sheer curtains allowed a lot of light into the room.

Readers can determine from context that *sheer* is similar in meaning to *transparent;* therefore *transparent* means "able to be seen through."

Identify Synonym Context Clues Circle the synonym context clues that help you determine the meaning of the underlined word in each sentence. Then write the meaning on the appropriate line.

1. The <u>amplified</u> sound of the band had so much of a boost that it annoyed all the neighbors.

   Meaning: _____

2. The little boy was <u>conscious</u> of the animal's footsteps and also aware of its loud growl.

   Meaning: _____

3. The rock <u>protruded</u> from the side of the cliff, jutting out about a hundred feet.

   Meaning: _____

4. The new engine was so <u>efficient</u> that it was an effective way to power the boat.

   Meaning: _____

5. The horse was so <u>gaunt</u> that we could see the ribs through its scrawny chest.

   Meaning: _____

6. The children were <u>enthralled</u> by the show; they were especially fascinated by the puppets' actions.

   Meaning: _____

7. Many plants and trees didn't survive the <u>aridity</u> of the summer drought.

   Meaning: _____

8. The <u>innocuous</u> insect was so harmless that the little boy wasn't afraid to pick it up.

   Meaning: _____

Analogies

An **analogy** compares the relationships between the words in two word pairs. The relationship between the two words in the first pair is the same as the relationship between the two words in the second pair.

EAR : HEAR : : _____

a. chin: lips   b. cheeks : face   c. mouth : taste   d. eyebrow : frown

Answer *c* best completes the sample analogy because an ear *hears,* and a mouth *tastes.* The analogy is read this way: *"Ear* is to *hear* as *mouth* is to *taste."*

Complete Analogies Circle the letter of the word pair that best completes each analogy.

1. BEAR : DEN : :
   a. bee : hive   b. car : road   c. train : track   d. hill : valley

2. PRETTY : BEAUTIFUL : :
   a. ugly : pretty   b. warm : hot   c. short : tall   d. free : freedom

3. CHAIR : SIT : :
   a. hard : soft   b. bed : sleep   c. lovely : nice   d. sun : light

4. APPEARANCE : LOOK : :
   a. employment : job   b. store : clothes   c. large : small   d. toe : foot

5. FARMER : TRACTOR : :
   a. road : ditch   b. song : verse   c. book : pen   d. pilot : plane

6. PAW : DOG : :
   a. open : shut   b. fin : fish   c. see : hear   d. arm : neck

7. ANGER : HOSTILITY : :
   a. weakness : strength   b. courage : bravery   c. full : narrow   d. top : whole

8. HAMMER : TOOL : :
   a. telephone : cord   b. helicopter : aircraft   c. monitor : computer   d. light : electricity

9. HAPPINESS : SADNESS : :
   a. huge : oversized   b. novel : character   c. generous : miserly   d. sickness : weakness

10. BROCCOLI : VEGETABLE : :
    a. cup : saucer   b. apple : fruit   c. nail : hammer   d. friendship : hatred

Context Clues

Context clues help readers figure out the meaning of unfamiliar words. Sometimes these context clues can be a word or a group of words that makes a comparison or contrast with the unfamiliar word.

> The winning team was <u>exuberant</u>, while the losing team seemed very depressed.

The word *depressed* is contrasted with *exuberant*, which readers can then conclude means "high-spirited or lively."

Use Comparison and Contrast Context Clues Use comparison or contrast context clues to determine the meaning of the underlined word in each sentence. Write the meaning of the underlined word on the blank line.

1. The article was divided into <u>installments</u>, instead of being printed in its entirety, to keep the readers interested.

   Meaning: _____

2. Usually the boy understood his friend; but today he was <u>baffled</u> by his actions.

   Meaning: _____

3. The little girl approached the dog with <u>trepidation</u>, unlike her older sister who didn't fear the animal.

   Meaning: _____

4. The small business, unlike its major competitor, a huge <u>conglomerate</u>, was unable to cope with the rapid increase in expenses.

   Meaning: _____

5. The lake was <u>contaminated</u> with dangerous chemicals, and therefore was no longer clean enough to swim in.

   Meaning: _____

6. First the man <u>swindled</u> people in one city; then he cheated his new business partners in another town.

   Meaning: _____

7. At first, the water <u>cascaded</u> gently over the rocks, but then it fell swiftly and without interference into the lake below.

   Meaning: _____

8. The neighbor was <u>antagonistic</u> one minute, but very friendly the next.

   Meaning: _____

Using Reference Materials

Reference materials, such as dictionaries, glossaries, and thesauruses, are very helpful in determining word meaning. However, a dictionary entry may include several possible meanings for a word. The context in which a word is used in a sentence will determine which meaning is most appropriate.

> Because he was tired, the man was in a bad <u>humor</u>.

The appropriate definition of *humor,* based on the context of this sentence, is "mood or state of mind."

Use Reference Materials to Determine Meanings For the underlined word in each of the following sentences, write your own definition based on context clues in the sentence. Then look up the word in a dictionary and write the most appropriate dictionary definition in the space provided.

1. The harried woman stopped in the store, looked at the clothes in a <u>cursory</u> way, and quickly left.

   My definition: _____

   Dictionary definition: _____

2. Because no one had repaired the house in many years, it became <u>dilapidated</u>.

   My definition: _____

   Dictionary definition: _____

3. The two countries signed a <u>reciprocal</u> trade agreement that benefitted both nations equally.

   My definition: _____

   Dictionary definition: _____

4. The <u>bellicose</u> general, eager to begin battle, ordered his army to attack the village.

   My definition: _____

   Dictionary definition: _____

5. The child was so <u>diffident</u> that she could not bring herself to talk to the other children at the birthday party.

   My definition: _____

   Dictionary definition: _____

Idioms

An **idiom** is an expression that has a special meaning which cannot be understood merely from the meanings of the individual words. Often readers can use context clues to figure out what an unfamiliar idiom means.

> The man was so angry when he realized he had a flat tire that he <u>flew off the handle</u> and kicked the car.

From the context of this sentence a reader would probably conclude that the idiom *flew off the handle* means "lost his temper."

Use Context Clues to Understand Idioms Use context clues to figure out the meaning of the underlined idiom in each sentence below. Write the meaning of the idiom on the blank line.

1. After hiking all day, the exhausted camper went back to his tent and <u>hit the sack</u>.

   _____

2. Our coach was so furious at the team's sloppiness that he really <u>blew a fuse</u>.

   _____

3. When we realized the factory was polluting the river, we <u>blew the whistle</u> on the owners.

   _____

4. The new house just doesn't <u>hold a candle</u> to the stately mansion it replaced.

   _____

5. The thief agreed to <u>come clean</u> to the police about his role in the robbery.

   _____

6. That store owner tried to <u>pull the wool over the eyes</u> of his customers by selling used clothing and pretending it was new.

   _____

7. The athlete, who had tried out for the football team five times, finally <u>threw in the towel</u> and joined the soccer team.

   _____

8. The boy <u>turned over a new leaf</u> and became an excellent student.

   _____

The Connotative Power of Words

The **connotation** of a word is the associated attitude or emotion it evokes in the reader. Connotations help writers suggest feelings or ideas without stating them literally.

> The snowstorm was <u>tenacious</u>, gripping the town for three days.

Synonyms of tenacious that could be used in this sentence are *persistent or stubborn. Tenacious,* however, has stronger and more dramatic connotations of "an unbreakable grip," which makes the sentence more interesting.

Interpret Word Connotations Using a dictionary or thesaurus, chose a synonym to replace the underlined word in each sentence. Rewrite the sentence using this synonym.

1. The <u>spunky</u> child refused to be frightened by the neighborhood bully.

   Sentence: _____

   _____

2. The flower was so <u>beautiful</u> that the woman couldn't bear to pick it.

   Sentence: _____

   _____

3. The <u>gaudy</u> costume drew a great deal of attention at the party.

   Sentence: _____

   _____

4. The customer was <u>angry</u> when he discovered that his car couldn't be fixed.

   Sentence: _____

   _____

5. The candidate had worked hard to earn the <u>approval</u> of the voters.

   Sentence: _____

   _____

Context Clues

Instead of relying on a dictionary, good readers often use the context of an unfamiliar word to understand its meaning. Context clues can be found in either the same sentence as the unknown word or in a nearby one.

The loud buzzer in the alarm clock <u>roused</u> the tired man from a deep sleep.

The words *loud buzzer* and *deep sleep* offer clues to the meaning of *roused,* which is "to awaken."

Use Context Clues Using context clues, figure out the meaning of the underlined word in each sentence. Write the meaning of the word on the line, followed by the context clues you used to infer its meaning.

1. The student <u>embellished</u> her story with additional details make it more interesting.

   Meaning: _____   Context clues: _____

2. The police found out that the suspect had <u>fabricated</u> his story; he was lying to hide his part in the robbery.

   Meaning: _____   Context clues: _____

3. Because the man <u>scribbled</u> his name, no one could read his signature.

   Meaning: _____   Context clues: _____

4. The side of the car was crushed by the <u>collision</u> with the fire hydrant.

   Meaning: _____   Context clues: _____

5. I gazed at the <u>azure</u> sky, unable to believe how perfectly blue it was.

   Meaning: _____   Context clues: _____

6. The sick man kept his medicine in a small glass <u>vial</u> on the table beside his bed.

   Meaning: _____   Context clues: _____

7. Because the small fire was not put out promptly, it grew into a blazing <u>inferno</u> that destroyed the house.

   Meaning: _____   Context clues: _____

8. The icy roads <u>hindered</u> the travelers, causing delays in the trip.

   Meaning: _____   Context clues: _____

Idioms

An **idiom** is an expression that has a different meaning from the literal or dictionary meaning of each individual word. To figure out the meaning of an idiom, it is helpful to study the context, or the surrounding words, in which it is used.

After school, the students <u>hung out</u> at a coffee shop and talked for hours.

From the context of the sentence, a reader can conclude that the idiom *hung out* means "sat around idly."

Identify the Meanings of Idioms Use context clues to figure out the meaning of the underlined idiom in each sentence. Write the meaning on the blank line.

1. The woman <u>put on airs</u>, wearing expensive clothes and jewelry to impress her neighbors.

_____

2. The exciting news story <u>made the headlines</u> on Friday morning.

_____

3. The proud man was so sure he was right that he had to <u>eat humble pie</u> when he was proven wrong.

_____

4. The student really <u>hit the books</u> the week before her exams.

_____

5. When her children refused to help clean the kitchen, Mrs. Morgan <u>put her foot down</u> and made them work.

_____

6. The two senators, who often disagreed on the issues, didn't see <u>eye to eye</u> on the new transportation legislation.

_____

7. The police office <u>turned a deaf ear</u> to the driver who insisted that he had stopped at the red light.

_____

8. After practicing hard for weeks, the swimmer finally <u>made the grade</u> and was allowed to join the team.

_____

Context Clues

Context clues in a sentence can help readers infer the meaning of an unfamiliar word.

The author's <u>memoir</u> focused on her childhood experiences.

From the context of the sentence, a reader could conclude that a *memoir* is "an account of personal experiences."

Use Context Clues to Determine Meaning Circle the context clues that help you infer the meaning of the underlined word in each sentence. Then use the word in an original sentence.

1. The <u>boisterous</u> group made so much noise the manager asked them to leave the restaurant.

   Sentence: _____

   _____

2. Tim's younger brother <u>resented</u> all the attention Tim received after winning the contest.

   Sentence: _____

   _____

3. The actress stood alone on the stage and delivered a very dramatic <u>monologue</u>.

   Sentence: _____

   _____

4. Sally refused to let anyone read her diary because it contained her most <u>intimate</u> thoughts.

   Sentence: _____

   _____

5. The <u>succinctness</u> of the poem expressed an important idea in just a few lines.

   Sentence: _____

   _____

6. The injured man tried to describe what happened, but he couldn't <u>articulate</u> his feelings about the accident.

   Sentence: _____

   _____

Antonyms

An **antonym**—a word with an opposite meaning—can provide a context clue to an unfamiliar word. In the sentence below, the context of the word *verbose* provides clues to its meaning.

The man's <u>verbose</u> speech continued so long that we got bored and fell asleep.

Once aware of the word's meaning, a reader can select an antonym for *verbose*. One antonym is *brief*.

Find Antonyms The vocabulary words listed below are in the story "Wasps' Nest" by Agatha Christie. Find and write the meaning for each word from its context within the story. Then circle the best antonym from the three possibilities given for each vocabulary word listed below.

1. absurd _____

Antonyms   a. logical   b. wild   c. silly

2. fathom _____

Antonyms   a. measurement   b. misinterpret   c. think

3. foreboding _____

Antonyms   a. premonition   b. conclusion   c. theory

4. hospitable _____

Antonyms   a. generous   b. courageous   c. rude

5. impersonally _____

Antonyms   a. aloof   b. friendly   c. genuine

6. languorous _____

Antonyms   a. slow   b. determined   c. energetic

7. lull _____

Antonyms   a. continuation   b. interruption   c. disturbance

8. resolutely _____

Antonyms   a. accidentally   b. consciously   c. experimentally

9. slacken _____

Antonyms   a. increase   b. press   c. slow

10. suitor _____

Antonyms   a. date   b. enemy   c. acquaintance

Synonyms

Readers can identify relationships in word meanings through **synonyms**—words that have similar meanings. Substituting one synonym for another may slightly alter the meaning of a sentence. In the example below, the word *chancy* is replaced with its synonym *dangerous.*

Climbing the steep, towering mountain in icy weather was <u>chancy</u>.

Climbing the steep, towering mountain in icy weather was <u>dangerous</u>.

The use of the word *dangerous* slightly alters the meaning of the sentence. *Dangerous* makes the climb more perilous than *chancy.*

Substitute Synonyms Cross out each underlined word below and write a synonym above it. On the lines following each sentence, write how the synonym changed the meaning of the sentence.

1. The teacher <u>instructed</u> the students to exit quickly during a fire drill.

   _____

2. When asked if he threw a snowball at his friend, Jason told a <u>fib</u>.

   _____

3. Once the snow melts into a brown slush, the city begins to look quite <u>unattractive</u>.

   _____

4. Certain foods, including pomegranates, may <u>stain</u> fabric.

   _____

5. While driving on a highway, the deliveryman lost control of his truck and <u>slid</u> off the road.

   _____

6. The young people <u>lingered</u> for almost an hour in front of the museum.

   _____

7. <u>Waiting</u> until the last minute to complete an important assignment is inadvisable.

   _____

8. Most still life artists are <u>vigilant</u> about the placement of objects in their paintings.

   _____

Context Clues

The context of a sentence can help readers determine the meaning of an unfamiliar word. A context clue sometimes restates the meaning of a difficult word in easier language. In the example below, the circled context clue restates the word *vivarium*, and helps to determine its meaning.

> Captive animals living in <u>vivariums</u> are fortunate, as these
>
> (natural habitat enclosures) resemble their own environment.

It is clear from the context that *vivarium* means a natural habitat enclosure.

Find Context Clues In each sentence below, circle the context clue that restates the meaning of the underlined word.

1. Many people learn best <u>aurally</u>, that is, by hearing the information.

2. The harsh verbal scolding, or <u>castigation</u>, of the man was not necessary.

3. The speaker's <u>egotistical</u> attitude was obvious to the audience, which was offended by this display of extreme conceit.

4. It is not uncommon that a crime remains temporarily <u>enigmatic</u> to police; that is, puzzling to figure out.

5. Jason's teacher gave an <u>intimation</u> that he would receive a scholarship, a hint that sent his confidence soaring.

6. Sherpa guides are <u>indispensable</u> in the Himalayas. In other words, they are absolutely essential.

7. The witness's <u>skewed</u> testimony—or misrepresentation of the facts—was obvious to the jurors.

8. The child's <u>facetious</u> comments were so humorous, we thought that he was destined to be a comedian.

9. An <u>ungainly</u> appearance does not always mean that a person lacks grace.

10. Mount St. Helens' eruption was a <u>cataclysmic</u> event, an overwhelmingly destructive force that permanently altered the surrounding ecosystem.

Context Clues

Even without looking up a definition, readers can infer the meaning of an unfamiliar word from context clues. One type of context clue is **restatement,** which uses slightly easier words to rephrase a more difficult word. In the example below, the word *leeward* is restated by the circled context clue.

The leeward side of the Polynesian island, even though

(situated away from the wind,) was still severely damaged

by the sudden storm.

Find Restatements In each sentence below, circle the context clue or restatement for the underlined word. Then, on the lines provided, write a new sentence using the underlined word.

1. Even though the young orchestra members would be long remembered for the cacophony that filled the music hall, this chaotic sound was endearing to their greatest admirers—their parents.

   _____

   _____

2. The calloused behavior of the country's dictator angered its citizens, who finally rose up against the ruler's cruel and insensitive actions.

   _____

   _____

3. Although many young people eagerly anticipate their matriculation into college, the actual day of enrollment and registration can be nerve-racking.

   _____

   _____

4. The elderly woman's prodigal spending needed to be monitored, as her extreme generosity had almost drained her bank account.

   _____

   _____

5. Although the manager realized that her interviewee's statement was mendacious, she did not indicate that she knew his assertion was false.

   _____

   _____

Word Origins

The **origin** of a word is the earliest recorded history of its use. For example, the word *note* is based upon the Middle English word *noten,* which is taken from the Old French word *noter,* which is taken from the Latin word *notare,* which means "to mark or note." From the English verb *note* come the adjectives *noted* and *noteworthy,* and the adverbs *notably* and *noteworthily.* All relate to the original meaning of the word's origin—"to mark or note."

Find Word Origins Use a dictionary to look up each word in the first column of the chart below. In the second column, write the word's origin (select one origin if there are several) and the meaning of the origin. In the third column, write a brief explanation of the relationship between the meaning of the word's origin and the present meaning of the word.

Word	Origin/Meaning	Relationship between origin and present meaning
1. cavalcade		
2. eulogy		
3. energy		
4. affluent		
5. simulate		

Context Clues

Sometimes the meaning of an unfamiliar word can be determined by analyzing substitute words such as **antonyms—**words with opposite or nearly opposite meanings—in the surrounding text. These words may serve as context clues. For example, in the following sentence, the words *banal* and *inspiring* both describe speeches. The context of the sentence informs the reader that these two words are opposite.

The chairperson's welcoming speech was banal, unlike his predecessor's inspiring address last year.

Banal is an antonym of *inspiring,* and means "boring."

Use Antonyms as Context Clues In each sentence below, circle the antonym that serves as a context clue for the underlined word. On the lines following each sentence, write a brief definition of the underlined word followed by a sentence containing that word.

1. The credence we placed in the witness's original statement gradually changed to distrust when we discovered the dishonesty of his subsequent statements.

Definition: _____

Sentence: _____

2. As a young child, Jason was very sociable, but lately he has become quite shy.

Definition: _____

Sentence: _____

3. Many say that there is not a cowardly bone in the body of an intrepid explorer.

Definition: _____

Sentence: _____

4. Olympic ski racers must be indefatigable; if ever they lacked energy, their competitors would pass them in a split second.

Definition: _____

Sentence: _____

5. The prosecution's cogent argument contrasted sharply with the confusing case presented by the defense.

Definition: _____

Sentence: _____

Denotation and Connotation

Many words have both a denotative and a connotative meaning. **Denotation** is a word's literal meaning or dictionary definition. **Connotation** is the attitudes, or emotions that a word evokes. For example, in the following sentence, the denotation of the word *left* is "departed." In the context of the sentence, *left* implies that the captain exited his ship without urgency.

> The captain <u>left</u> his ship once it had run ashore.

When *left* is changed to the synonym *abandoned,* the connotation changes.

> The captain <u>abandoned</u> his ship once it had run ashore.

The word *abandoned* implies that the captain had a compelling reason to leave the ship and perhaps even deserted the ship.

Identify Denotation and Connotation After each phrase below are three synonyms with different connotations. On the line within each phrase, write the synonym that best completes the phrase. On the lines below each phrase, explain why the word is the best choice.

1. won over by a(n) _____ speaker   (active, vigorous, dynamic)

   _____

   _____

2. the _____ eighty-year-old who competed in today's marathon (active, vigorous, dynamic)

   _____

   _____

3. watching the _____ falling snow   (quiet, soundless, still)

   _____

   _____

4. celebrated their anniversary by _____ at an elegant restaurant   (eating, dining, chowing down)

   _____

   _____

5. such a _____ argument that even the opponents dropped their objections   (valid, sound, convincing)

   _____

   _____

Suffixes

A **suffix** is a letter or combination of letters added to the end of a word that changes the word's meaning. The following are some types of words created by suffixes:

Plurals of nouns   *book + -s* makes the noun plural

Tenses of verbs   *talk + -ed* changes the verb to past tense

Comparative and superlative forms of adjectives and adverbs
great + -er or *-est*   *slow + -er* or *-est*

Adverbs: adding *-ly* can change an adjective to an adverb as in the following:
quiet + -ly = quietly

The meaning and part of speech of most words can be changed by adding different suffixes, as in these examples:

simple + -fy = simplify (adjective to verb)

simple + -fication = simplification (adjective to noun)

simple + -ly = simply (adjective to adverb)

Find Suffixes For each word below, identify and write the meaning of the base word and of the suffix. Then write a brief definition of each word.

Word	Base/Meaning	Suffix/Meaning	Definition
1. languorous			
2. forboding			
3. resolutely			
4. abashed			
5. dryness			
6. dispenser			
7. grievous			
8. spacious			
9. cellular			
10. alphabetize			

Context Clues

Readers can determine the meaning of an unfamiliar word in a sentence by thinking about the word's **context,** the words in the sentence that provide a clue to its meaning. In the example below, the meaning of the word *altercation* can be determined by the sentence context.

> The politicians' altercation ended peacefully, in spite of the way their unfortunate war of words had begun.

The context clue for *altercation* is "war of words."

Find Meanings of Unfamiliar Words Circle the context clue in each sentence below that suggests the meaning of the underlined word.

1. A huge crevice had formed in the earth's crust—one similar to the nearby abyss formed thousands of years ago.

2. In England, baby carriages are called prams, a word that comes from perambulator.

3. The man's egregious error was gambling away his entire savings, a foolish act that had long-lasting effects.

4. The witness's glib testimony did not fool the jury, who caught on quickly to his manner of smooth talking.

5. Alana, a true Francophile, was obsessed with all things French, including food, customs, and language.

6. A metronome, with its swinging pendulum that keeps time, is essential for most young musicians.

7. In America, the fifty states are somewhat autonomous and may make certain decisions independently of the federal government.

8. As an adroit speaker, Will knew that this valued ability of skillful speaking would serve him well as a lawyer.

9. Certain people model altruistic behavior as they put other's needs above their own.

10. Unfortunately, the horse could not complete his capriole, as the instant he came down from this complex jump, he twisted his hoof.

Analogies

A word analogy shows a relationship between two pairs of words. In an analogy, the relationship between the first pair of words is the same as the relationship between the second pair. In the example below, *admire* is the opposite of *despise.* Therefore, the word that best completes the analogy with *calm* should also have the same relationship—in this case, the opposite meaning.

ADMIRE : DESPISE : : _____ : calm

a. soothe   b. frantic   c. dislike

Frantic completes the analogy because it has the same relationship to *calm* as *admire* does to *despise;* the words in each pair are opposite in meaning.

Complete Analogies Determine the relationship between the first pair of words in the analogies below. Then look for the same relationship to complete the answer for the second pair. Write the word that completes each analogy on the line provided.

1. ANNOY : INFURIATE : : speak : _____
   a. sigh   b. shriek   c. laugh

2. MALE : FRATERNITY : : female : _____
   a. paternity   b. maternity   c. sorority

3. SANTA FE : NEW MEXICO : : _____ : Italy
   a. London   b. Rome   c. Paris

4. SIX : THIRTY : : one hundred : _____
   a. one thousand   b. two hundred   c. five hundred

5. FLAP : WING : : wave : _____
   a. hand   b. plane   c. water

6. SPLINTER : WOOD : : _____ : bread
   a. flour   b. loaf   c. crumb

7. EXTINCT : DINOSAUR : : outdated : _____
   a. Model-T   b. letter   c. telephone

8. LEASH : DOG : : _____ : horse
   a. saddle   b. rein   c. stirrups

9. EXPEL : ADMIT : : approve : _____
   a. ask   b. destroy   c. disapprove

10. STUPENDOUS : MAGNIFICENT : : saturated : _____
    a. dried   b. wonderful   c. drenched

The Connotative Power of Words

A word's **connotation** is the emotional overtones that it carries and the associations it calls to mind. Synonyms share denotations but often carry different connotations. Writers choose words with connotations that further their purpose for writing. For example, this sentence from Tony Hillerman's essay "The Great Taos Bank Robbery" contains words with connotations that set a tone of tension:

> By noon, the population of Taos—normally about 1,850—had been <u>swollen</u> by the <u>influx</u> of various types of officers.

The words *swollen* and *influx* connote large numbers of people flowing into the small town in an unrestrained way. The following sentence uses synonyms for *swollen* and *influx.*

> By noon, the population of Taos—normally about 1,850—had <u>grown</u> by the <u>arrival</u> of various types of officers.

Notice how neutral and bland the meaning becomes with the use of the words *grown* and *arrival.*

Identify Connotations In the following sentences from Hillerman's essay, underline at least one word from each sentence with strong connotations that help you visualize the action, characters, and setting of the story—or that help set the mood. Use a thesaurus to find a synonym for each word you underlined and write it above that word. Now reread the sentences and determine if your synonyms have the same effect as the original wording.

1. Taos is a tolerant village, well accustomed to whimsy.

2. It has been said that if the late James Thurber had been raised here he
   would never have celebrated the antics of his family in print, since what
   seems outlandish in Columbus, Ohio, seems fairly normal in Taos.

3. In Taos a certain amount of eccentricity is required for conformity.

4. Interest among the spectators quickened, however, when some of them
   saw—or thought they saw—a pistol in the hand of the pseudo-woman.

5. The fleet-footed ones, who had beaten the rush to the tellers' windows and
   therefore left early, spread the news of this unusual sight around Taos Plaza.

Context Clues

Context clues can provide comparisons or contrasts within a sentence that help to determine word meanings. In the following sentence, a **comparison** context clue helps determine the meaning for the word *gregarious.*

Maggie is very <u>gregarious</u>, just like her sister who is also extremely friendly.

The context of this sentence compares *gregarious* to "extremely friendly."

In the next sentence, a **contrasting** context clue helps determine the meaning for the word *lachrymose.*

The kindergarten teacher expected the children to be <u>lachrymose</u> their first day, but to her surprise, there was not a single tear shed.

The context of this sentence contrasts *lachrymose* to "not a single tear shed." This clue helps readers to infer that *lachrymose* means tearful or weepy.

Find Comparison and Contrast Context Clues In the following sentences, circle the context clue for each underlined word. Underline *Comparison* or *Contrast* depending on the type of context clue. On the lines provided, write a brief definition for each underlined word.

1. Oddly, the two best friends had completely different outlooks on life; one was a <u>pessimist</u>, while the other searched for the good in everything.

   Comparison/Contrast   Definition: _____

2. For his recent paper, Jonathan's research notes are <u>voluminous</u>, unlike his previous ones, which were scanty at best.

   Comparison/Contrast   Definition: _____

3. Alison's flute concert filled the auditorium with <u>euphonious</u> sounds, just what we expected from this young musician who always produces music pleasing to the ear.

   Comparison/Contrast   Definition: _____

4. It is advisable to avoid <u>cliches</u> like the plague! Instead, try to use imaginative words and phrases in your written work.

   Comparison/Contrast   Definition: _____

5. The dog's ability to remain <u>complacent</u> while being groomed was a miracle, especially given his wild behavior as a puppy.

   Comparison/Contrast   Definition: _____

Context Clues

Sometimes, the meaning of an unfamiliar word can be determined by analyzing a cause-and-effect relationship in the text. This relationship, also called *causal,* may be stated directly or implied. In the following sentence, there is a causal relationship between the word *deterred* and arriving late.

> Deterred by a horrendous snowstorm on the East Coast, the plane arrived four hours late to Miami.

The causal relationship of this sentence implies that *deterred* means delayed.

Find Causal Relationships In the sentences below, circle the context clue that provides a meaning for the underlined word and demonstrates a causal relationship. Write a definition for each underlined word and then use it in a sentence.

1. Unaware of the young child's <u>hippophobia</u>, her uncle got as far as the entrance to a horse stable before she started crying from fear.

   Definition: _____

   Sentence: _____

2. Because some societies are <u>matriarchal</u>, women control the household, the tribe, and often the commerce.

   Definition: _____

   Sentence: _____

3. Failing in his attempt to appear <u>indifferent</u> while his students expressed opposing views, the professor literally had to hold his hand over his mouth.

   Definition: _____

   Sentence: _____

4. Since the music was <u>somniferous</u>, it was used during naptime at the nursery school—some children actually fell asleep!

   Definition: _____

   Sentence: _____

5. With a nod of his head, the third-base coach gave the runner his <u>tacit</u> approval to steal second base.

   Definition: _____

   Sentence: _____

VOCABU-
LARY

87

Analogies

Understanding analogies helps readers to improve their vocabulary and reasoning skills. An **analogy** is a word statement that consists of two pairs of words that share a similar relationship. For example, the analogy "AUTHOR : MANUSCRIPT : : _____ : music" is read "an author is to a manuscript as *blank* is to music." Stating the relationship of the existing pair will help you determine how to complete the analogy: "An author creates a manuscript as a *composer* creates music."

Complete Analogies Choose a word from the box that best completes each analogy. Use a dictionary as needed.

beguiling	chide	contender	disconsolate	entice
amused	snare	stealthy	succumb	vile

1. FRIGHTENED : THREATENING : : charmed : _____

2. _____ : TRAP : : village : town

3. PLEASING : _____ : : sensitive : callous

4. _____ : burglar : : bold : warrior

5. RESIST : _____ : : innocence : guilt

6. AMUSE : ENTERTAIN : : lure : _____

7. SAD : _____ : : happy : joyful

8. FIGHTER : _____ : : sea : ocean

9. PRAISE : ACCOMPLISHMENT : : _____ : disobedience

10. OFFENDED : INSULT : : _____ : joke

Antonyms

An **antonym** of a word is a word that has the opposite meaning. For example, *respect* is an antonym for *disdain. Admiration* and *honor* are also antonyms for *disdain.* Knowing the antonym of a word means that you can use that word with increased mastery.

Supply Antonyms Write at least one antonym for each of the following words. Use a dictionary or thesaurus as needed.

Word	Antonym(s)
1. formidable	
2. ponderous	
3. construct	
4. fidelity	
5. uncommunicative	
6. innovative	
7. entice	
8. disconsolate	
9. unite	
10. chaos	
11. dwindle	
12. peril	
13. travail	
14. dire	
15. anguish	

Context Clues

Readers must often rely on context to determine meanings of words and phrases used in figurative language. **Figurative language** is language that describes one thing as if it were something else. Consider the underlined word in the following lines spoken by Polyphemus in Book 9 of the *Odyssey* (lines 157–159).

> What brings you here by sea ways—a fair traffic?
> Or are you wandering rogues, who <u>cast</u> your lives
> like dice, and ravage other folk by sea?

Readers can use the following steps to determine the meaning of *cast.*

1. Identify the figurative language: "cast your lives like dice."

2. Determine how the context clues suggest the meaning of *cast*: Dice are used in games of chance; dice are thrown.

3. Suggest a meaning for *cast* based on context. *Cast* here means "throw."

4. Try the suggested meaning to see if it works: "rogues, who <u>throw</u> their lives around like dice, and ravage other folk" makes sense.

Determine Meanings of Figurative Language Use the steps above to interpret each example of figurative language underlined below. Write down what you do at each step.

1. [The Cyclops] whisked away his great stone door/to let his sheep go through—but he, behind,/reset the stone <u>as one would cap a quiver</u>. (Book 9, lines 217–219)

   Context clues: _____

   Meaning of *cap:* _____

   Meaning in context: _____

2. [We lugged the stick] near the Cyclops/. . . lifted it, and rammed it/deep in <u>his crater eye</u>. (Book 9, lines 289–292)

   Context clues: _____

   Meaning of *crater:* _____

   Meaning in context: _____

3. But you—small, pitiful and <u>twiggy</u>—/you put me down with wine, you blinded me. (Book 9, lines 429–430)

   Context Clues: _____

   Meaning of *twiggy:* _____

   Meaning in context: _____

Latin Roots

Many English words have Latin origins. For that reason, many of the words used in English translations of the *Odyssey* have Latin roots. For example, the word *avenge* comes from the French word *vengier,* which comes from the Latin *vindicare,* meaning "to vindicate." *Vindicate* means "to justify," or "to prove right"; to *avenge* means "to exact a penalty for a wrong that has been committed."

Research Latin Roots Many dictionaries include brief etymologies, or word histories. Find and record the etymology of each word below, being sure to include its Latin root. Then explain how the meaning of each word is related to the meaning of its root.

1. adversary

    Etymology: _____

    Explanation: _____

2. appall

    Etymology: _____

    Explanation: _____

3. quest

    Etymology: _____

    Explanation: _____

4. desolate

    Etymology: _____

    Explanation: _____

5. contempt

    Etymology: _____

    Explanation: _____

6. formidable

    Etymology: _____

    Explanation: _____

Using Synonyms

A **synonym** is a word that has the same or nearly the same meaning as another word. Knowing a word's synonyms can help you find precisely the right word to complete a sentence.

> The newcomer was _____ and remained indifferent despite the neighbors' attempts to befriend her.

If you wanted to complete this sentence with a synonym for *indifferent,* the word *apathetic* would be a good choice.

Supply Synonyms To complete each sentence, choose a word from the box that is a synonym for the underlined word. Use a dictionary or thesaurus as needed.

lavished	gall	dithering	turmoil	restitution
contemptible	rash	conflict	justification	desolation

1. Many people commented on the group's <u>indecisiveness</u>; they felt frustrated

   by the fruitless _____.

2. Several abandoned cabins added to the site's atmosphere of <u>emptiness</u>

   and _____.

3. <u>Reckless</u> behavior often results from _____ decisions.

4. The <u>struggle</u> for power erupted into a military _____.

5. His <u>brashness</u> matches her _____.

6. The man tried to give a reasonable <u>explanation</u> of his actions, but there is no

   _____ for such rudeness.

7. Viewers _____ praise on the performance and

   <u>showered</u> compliments on the cast.

8. The crew's _____ created <u>chaos</u> on the sinking ship.

9. That clerk should be fired for her <u>detestable</u> attitude and _____

   behavior.

10. I offered to tend my neighbors' lawn as <u>repayment</u> for driving over it, but they

    declined to accept my method of _____.

Context Clues

Readers must often rely on context to determine the meanings of words and phrases, including figurative language and archaic expressions. For example, consider Juliet's use of the word *division* in *The Tragedy of Romeo and Juliet,* Act 3, Scene 5.

Some say the lark makes sweet <u>division</u>;
This doth not so, for she divideth us.

The different meanings of *division* can be inferred by examining the context of the lines. Juliet is unhappy that dawn will part her from Romeo. The figurative meaning of *division* is "melody," inferred from *lark* (a type of bird) and *makes* (sings). The lark's melody divides or "separates" the lovers by signaling the coming day.

Use Context Clues to Infer Meaning Use context clues to infer the meaning of each underlined word or phrase. Write that meaning on the first line. Then explain in writing how the context clues helped you infer the meaning.

1. Juliet to Romeo: . . . the mask of night is on my face;/Else would a maiden blush <u>bepaint</u> my cheek. (Act Two, Scene 2, lines 94–95)

   Meaning: _____

   Context clues: _____

2. Romeo: How silver-sweet sound lovers' tongues by night,/Like softest music to <u>attending</u> ears! (Act Two, Scene 2, lines 183–184)

   Meaning: _____

   Context clues: _____

3. Romeo to Tybalt: I do protest I never injured thee,/But love thee better than thou canst <u>devise</u>. (Act Three, Scene 1, lines 71–72)

   Meaning: _____

   Context clues: _____

4. Mercutio, after being stabbed: A plague o' both your houses!/They have made <u>worms' meat</u> of me. (Act Three, Scene 1, lines 113–114)

   Meaning: _____

   Context clues: _____

Using Reference Materials

A dictionary is a helpful reference tool for determining the precise meaning of a word. For example, if you needed to know the meaning of the word *kin,* a dictionary would reveal that it means "one's relatives; family."

Research Word Meanings Below are brief excerpts from Shakespeare's *The Tragedy of Romeo and Juliet.* Use a dictionary to look up the meaning of each underlined word and record the meaning on the line. Be prepared to search for the base form of each word first (for example, the base of *beseeming* is *beseem*).

1. <u>beseeming</u> ornaments (Act One, Scene 1, line 101)

   Meaning: _____

2. to part your <u>cankered</u> hate (Act One, Scene 1, line 103)

   Meaning: _____

3. stole into the <u>covert</u> of the wood (Act One, Scene 1, line 133)

   Meaning: _____

4. <u>baleful</u> weeds and precious-juiced flowers (Act Two, Scene 3, line 9)

   Meaning: _____

5. [where he] Doth <u>couch</u> his limbs (Act Two, Scene 3, line 40)

   Meaning: _____

6. We met, we <u>wooed</u>, and made exchange of vow. (Act Two, Scene 3, line 67)

   Meaning: _____

7. did read by <u>rote</u> (Act Two, Scene 3, line 96)

   Meaning: _____

8. <u>driveling</u> love (Act Two, Scene 4, line 95)

   Meaning: _____

9. By my <u>troth</u> (Act Two, Scene 4, line 122)

   Meaning: _____

10. I <u>trow</u> (Act Two, Scene 5, line 67)

    Meaning: _____

Word Origins

One of the reasons that Shakespeare's vocabulary was so rich and varied is that his vocabulary was based on several languages, including Latin, Greek, and Anglo-Saxon, or Old English. Word histories, or **etymologies,** are included in many comprehensive dictionaries. For example, the word *cunning,* which now means "crafty," "ingenious," or "cute," comes from Middle English *connen,* "to know," from Anglo-Saxon *cunnan.*

Research Word Origins Look up the following words. Write down the origin of each, including the meaning of the original word if given.

1. tomorrow

   Origin: _____

2. audience

   Origin: _____

3. heaven

   Origin: _____

4. prologue

   Origin: _____

5. pity

   Origin: _____

6. woe

   Origin: _____

7. dear

   Origin: _____

8. quarrel

   Origin: _____

9. meddle

   Origin: _____

10. slander

   Origin: _____

Using a Glossary

A **glossary** is like a dictionary, but it applies only to a limited subject, such as to one work of literature or all the works of one author. This narrow focus allows the writer of a glossary to supply precise meanings of words as they appear in context. For example, the glossary definition of *protest* as used by Shakespeare is "to declare with solemnity, proclaim publicly, promise, vow," not "to object," as commonly used today.

Use a Glossary Look up the following words in a glossary of Shakespearean words or in the SourceBook for *The Tragedy of Romeo and Juliet.* Write the precise meaning of each word in its given context. All the words below appear in the glossary of *The Riverside Shakespeare.* You will sometimes need to infer a word's meaning from a variation of the word; for example, define *strange* from its variation, *strangely.*

1. humor (Act 1, Scene 1, line 137)

   Meaning: _____

2. fair (Act 2, Scene 1, line 13)

   Meaning: _____

3. strange (Act 2, Scene 2, line 111)

   Meaning: _____

4. sweet (Act 2, Scene 2, line 131)

   Meaning: _____

5. suffer (Act 2, Scene 4, line 160)

   Meaning: _____

6. wreak (Act 3, Scene 5, line 113)

   Meaning: _____

7. abused (Act 4, Scene 1, line 33)

   Meaning: _____

8. copest (Act 4, Scene 1, line 83)

   Meaning: _____

9. cross (Act 4, Scene 3, line 5)

   Meaning: _____

Expanding Vocabulary

Reading Shakespeare provides a good opportunity to expand your vocabulary.
Although some Elizabethan words are not used today, many remain in current use. For
example, *beseech* means to "entreat or plead with," as in "The salesclerk <u>beseeched</u>
the irate customer, 'Have patience, please.'"

Apply New Words Write the Shakesperian meaning of each underlined word. Then
write a contemporary sentence using the word.

1. An infectious disease <u>reigned</u> over the city.

   Meaning: _____

   Sentence: _____

2. Do as I <u>bid</u> thee, go.

   Meaning: _____

   Sentence: _____

3. He lay under <u>yonder</u> yew tree.

   Meaning: _____

   Sentence: _____

4. Romeo called Juliet the "dearest <u>morsel</u> of earth."

   Meaning: _____

   Sentence: _____

5. Romeo decided to <u>sunder</u> himself.

   Meaning: _____

   Sentence: _____

6. . . . <u>inauspicious</u> stars

   Meaning: _____

   Sentence: _____

7. The <u>ensign</u> of beauty was in Juliet's red lips.

   Meaning: _____

   Sentence: _____

Answer Key

Copymaster 18
Context Clues
(Responses will vary. Sample responses are provided.)
1. thrifty: wisely economical; sparing
2. predicament: a problematic situation; dilemma
3. disconsolate: extremely dejected
4. incessantly: continuing without interruption
5. distressed: troubled

Copymaster 19
Context Clues
1. b
2. d
3. a
4. b
5. c

Copymaster 20
Word Origins
(Meanings and sentences will vary. Possible responses are provided.)
1. precede
   Meaning: to come, exist, or occur before in time
   Sentence: Traditionally, an engagement will precede a couple's marriage.
2. proceed
   Meaning: to go forward or onward, especially after an interruption; continue
   Sentence: After a brief power outage, the guest lecturer was able to proceed with his slide show.
3. access
   Meaning: a means of approaching, entering, exiting, or making use of; passage
   Sentence: The access to the game was blocked by the bulldozer.
4. cease
   Meaning: to put an end to; discontinue
   Sentence: She ceased paying attention to the radio announcer after a few minutes, turning her interest to the bird on the ledge.
5. ancestor
   Meaning: a person from whom one is descended
   Sentence: His ancestors had come to the United States from Italy, in the 1920s.

Copymaster 21
Antonyms
(Responses will vary. Sample responses are provided.)
1. puffy: rounded
2. stifle: to interrupt or cut off; to suppress
3. decay: the destruction or composition of organic matter as a result of bacterial or fungal action; rot
4. skirted: passed around rather than across or through
5. trailing: lagging behind

Copymaster 22
Context Clues
(Responses will vary. Sample responses are provided.)
1. audible: able to be heard
2. vigor: physical or mental strength, energy, or force
3. monotonous: tediously repetitious; boring
4. sterility: the condition of producing little or no vegetation; barren
5. bewilderment: confusion or disorientation

Copymaster 23
Prefixes
(Responses will vary. Sample responses are provided.)
1. multimedia: the combined use of several media, such as movies, slides, music, and lighting, especially for the purpose of education or entertainment
2. multicultural: of, relating to, or including several cultures
3. multidirectional: reaching out in several directions; operating or functioning in more than one direction
4. multipurpose: designed or used for several purposes
5. multinational: having operations, subsidiaries, or investments in several countries; of or involving several countries

Copymaster 24
Context Clues
(Responses will vary. Sample responses are provided.)
1. frantically: excitedly, frenziedly
2. lull: a relatively calm interval
3. maneuvered: manipulated into a desired position
4. cordial: friendly, gracious
5. wrenched: twisted or turned suddenly and forcibly; injured

Copymaster 25
Using Reference Materials
(Responses will vary. Sample responses are provided.)
1. radar: a method of detecting distant objects and determining their position, speed, or other characteristics by analysis of very high frequency radio waves reflected from their surfaces
2. hatch: a small door or opening
3. cutter: a small, lightly armed boat used by the Coast Guard
4. snorkel: a breathing apparatus used by skin divers, consisting of a long tube held in the mouth; used by divers for breathing while under water
5. rotors: a helicopter's assembly of rotating horizontal propeller blades

Copymaster 26
Connotation
(Responses will vary. Sample responses are provided.)
1. stinging/piercing; wounding; suffering keenly
2. blast/a violent explosion; a powerful hit or blow
3. lashed/whipped; thrashed; flailed
4. stilled/silenced, calmed
5. rattling/a sound in the throat sometimes made by a person who is near death

Copymaster 27
Using a Dictionary to Determine Precise Meanings
(Definitions and origins may vary. Sample responses are provided.)
Word/Meaning(s)/Origin
1. shabby/wearing threadbare clothing; worn-out; deteriorated in condition; despicable; unfair; of mediocre quality/from obsolete *shab,* scab, from Middle English *shab,* from Old English *sceabb*
2. laboriously/marked by or requiring long, hard work; industriously/Middle English, from Old French *laborieux,* from Latin *laboriosus,* from *labor,* labor
3. falter/waver; hesitate; stammer; stumble/Middle English, *falteren,* to stagger, possibly from Old Norse *faltrask,* to be puzzled, hesitate
4. subside/to sink to a lower or normal level; to sink or settle down; to sink to the bottom; decrease/from Latin *subsidere: sub-,* below; under; beneath, + *sidere,* to settle
5. calculated/determined by mathematical calculation; undertaken after careful estimation of the likely outcome; deliberate; likely/from Latin *calculus,* small stone used in reckoning

Copymaster 28
Antonyms
(Definitions will vary. Sample responses are provided.)
1. peered/circle antonym: glanced
   Definition: looked intently, searchingly, or with difficulty
2. reckless/circle antonym: careful
   Definition: heedless or careless
3. retired/circle antonym: approached
   Definition: to withdraw, as for rest or seclusion
4. eagerness/circle antonym: indifference
   Definition: full of interest, intense desire, or impatient expectancy
5. shattered/circle antonym: intact
   Definition: caused to break or burst suddenly into pieces, as with a violent blow

Copymaster 29
Using Context to Determine Meaning
(Responses will vary. Sample responses are provided.)
1. chipper: cheerful
2. infatuated: full of unreasoning love or attachment
3. luxury: something inessential but conducive to pleasure and comfort
4. unduly: excessively
5. sloppiness: untidiness; the absence of neatness

Copymaster 30
Analogies
1. b
2. d
3. c
4. a
5. d

Copymaster 31
Context Clues
(Meanings may vary. Sample responses are provided.)
Restated Word/Meaning of Word/Context Clues
1. zeal/ethusiastic devotion to a cause, an ideal, or a goal/circle: the second and third commas and the word *passion*
2. negligence/the act of paying little or no attention to something/circle: the first and second commas, the phrase *that is,* and the word *carelessness*
3. festive/of or relating to a festival/circle: the second and third commas and the phrase *or merry*
4. intercept/stop, seize, or interrupt the progress of something/circle: *In other words,* the comma, and the phrase *stopped the items from being delivered*
5. jeopardy/risk of loss or injury/circle: *danger or peril* and the comma and *meaning.*

Copymaster 32
Connotation
(Responses will vary. Sample responses are provided.)
Word/Denotation/Connotation
1. startled/alarmed, frightened, or surprised/the fear that you feel when loud noises awaken you from sleep
2. horrified/terrified, shocked/fear associated with scary movies or tales told around a campfire
3. desperate/extremely intense/a sense of urgency
4. terror/intense, overpowering fear/the feeling that a situation is out of control; horror movies
5. clamor/a loud, sustained noise/annoyance or fear

Copymaster 33
Using Reference Materials
(Sample synonyms are provided. Students' sentences will vary.)
1. retribution
   Synonyms: payback, avengement, recompense, reckoning, reward
2. abscond
   Synonyms: run away, make a break, vanish, sneak away, escape
3. gait
   Synonyms: bearing, walk, motion, movement, step
4. jest
   Synonyms: banter, joke, fool, josh, deride
5. obstinate
   Synonyms: stubborn, determined, cantankerous, indomitable, opinionated

Copymaster 34
Meanings of Roots
(Responses will vary. Sample responses are provided.)
1. descended: climbed down
2. intoxication: the condition of being under the influence of a poison or a chemical substance such as alcohol
3. insufferably: intolerably; unbearably
4. impose: to place or force someone
5. disturbed: troubled; upset

Copymaster 35
Synonyms
1. fashionable/trendy
2. stormy/inclement
3. tolerable/endurable
4. height/stature
5. devised/contrived

Copymaster 36
Context Clues
(Students' own definitions may vary but they should relate to the context clues. Dictionary definitions are provided.)
1. dismal
   Your definition: dreary
   Dictionary definition: causing gloom or depression; dreary
2. grimacing
   Your definition: frowning, scowling
   Dictionary definition: making a sharp distortion of the face expressive of pain, contempt, or disgust
3. deftly
   Your definition: skillfully
   Dictionary definition: quickly and skillfully
4. finicky
   Your definition: fussy, squeamish
   Dictionary definition: insisting capriciously on getting just what one wants; fastidious
5. parcel
   Your definition: package
   Dictionary definition: something wrapped up or packaged

Copymaster 37
Dialect
(Students' responses will vary. Sample responses are provided.)
1. blathering
   Rewrite: Sister Rita warned you that you would have to go upstairs if you talked again. We warned you to stop your foolish talking, but you wouldn't.
   Meaning of word: foolish or nonsensical talking
2. 'twas
   Rewrite: Seamus says that it was a truly terrible thing.
   Meaning of word: it was
3. 'twould;
   Rewrite: She says that it would upset you to think about how the government of England has treated the Irish people.
   Meaning of word: it would
4. missus
   Rewrite: My mom is sitting next to me. The nurse tells her that they don't usually allow mothers in the rooms.
   Meaning of word: ma'am—a polite way of speaking to a woman
5. by
   Rewrite: Take the boy, Seamus, remove him from this place.
   Meaning of word: boy

Copymaster 38
Antonyms
(Responses may vary. Sample responses are provided.)
1. communicate: talk
2. preventive: treating people before something happens
3. straightforward: precise words, honest and open dialogue
4. relief: sense of joy at being freed from something
5. faith: trust or confidence

Copymaster 39
Using a Dictionary
A. Answers may vary, depending on the source used.
   1. acquaintance: a person whom someone knows
   2. armada: a large group of moving things
   3. bantam: any of various breeds of small, domestic birds
   4. dilapidated: decayed, deteriorated
   5. enterprise: a risky or complicated undertaking
   6. glower: to stare at in anger
   7. inhabit: to live in
   8. mingle: to mix or bring together
   9. rummage: to search by handling the contents of something
   10. tabulate: to condense and list
B. 11. inhabit
   12. tabulate
   13. dilapidated
   14. acquaintance
   15. rummage

Copymaster 40
Idioms
(Meanings will vary. Sample responses are provided.)
1. pay attention to
2. fooling him, teasing him
3. too difficult to understand
4. a miniscule part of what is needed
5. tried out every plan or idea they could think of

Copymaster 41
Context Clues
(Definitions may vary. Sample responses are provided.)
1. cause: anticipate danger and behave cautiously/ effect: avoid problems altogether
   Definition: think or plan ahead
2. cause: new to the community/effect: endured a long and lonely summer
   Definition: survived
3. cause: phenomenal catch/effect: became captain of the team
   Definition: remarkable, outstanding
4. cause: no one answered the telephone/effect: became very agitated
   Definition: unsettled, disturbed
5. cause: not enthralled with our idea/effect: had to come up with a new plan
   Definition: excited by or pleased with

Copymaster 42
Context Clues
1. static
   Definition: unchanging
2. trembling
   Definition: responding to fear by shaking
3. erodes
   Definition: washes away
4. humid
   Definition: wet or full of water
5. tentative
   Definition: subject to change

Copymaster 43
Word Origins
(Responses will vary according to reference sources used. Sample responses are provided.)
Word/Definition/Origin
1. poise/to hold in balance/from Middle English *poisen,* to weigh
2. surmise/to make a guess without evidence/from Middle English *surmysen,* to accuse
3. accumulate/to gather or pile up/from Latin *cumukus,* heap
4. vagary/strange idea/from Latin *vagari,* to wander
5. aberration/an abnormality, a deviation from what is expected/from Latin *ab-,* from, + *errare,* to stray
6. bucolic/pastoral, characteristic of shepherds or flocks/from Greek *bous,* cow, and *kolos,* herdsman
7. deleterious/injurious, harmful/from Greek *deleisthai,* to harm
8. gossamer/soft, sheer fabric; also a film of cobwebs floating in the air or sitting on grass or bushes/from Old English *gos,* goose, + *sumor,* summer
9. naïve/lacking worldliness or sophistication/from Latin *nasci,* to be born
10. regale/to delight or entertain, to give pleasure/from Latin *gale,* pleasure

Copymaster 44
Context Clues
(Meanings may vary. Sample responses are provided.)
Word/Example Clues/Word Meaning
1. confronted/rushing at it with his spear/to stand up to
2. interminable/the long hours/endless
3. vanity/his proud stance, his boldly decorated attire/conceit, self-admiration
4. contempt/scornful curl of his lip, dismissive shrug of his shoulders/scorn
5. accolades/crisp salutes, applause, a medal/praise or other signs of respect

Copymaster 45
Antonyms
(Definitions may vary. Sample responses are provided.)
1. falter/antonym: sure-footed
   Definition: hesitate, stumble
2. affinity/antonym: dislike
   Definition: preference, liking
3. ravenous/antonym: gorged
   Definition: hungry, famished
4. inept/antonym: competent
   Definition: incompetent or bungling
5. felicitous/antonym: unsuitable
   Definition: appropriate, well-timed

Copymaster 46
Prefixes and Suffixes
(Responses will vary. Sample responses are provided.)
Prefix/Meaning/Words
1. *dis-*/not/disallow, dismiss
2. *com-*/together/comfort, comply
3. *in-*/into/ingrain, inside,
4. *un-*/not/unable, untie
5. *-ful*/full of/fearful, playful
6. *-less*/without/flawless, careless
7. *-hood*/condition, state, quality/childhood, statehood
8. *-ive*/performing or tending toward/active, defensive
9. *-ize*/become or cause to become/summarize, idealize
10. *-ist*/one that performs, one that makes, operates, plays/pianist, artist

Copymaster 47
Analogies
1. b.; Relationship expressed: synonym
2. c.; Relationship expressed: cause to effect
3. a.; Relationship expressed: part to whole
4. b.; Relationship expressed: antonym
5. a.; Relationship expressed: synonym

Copymaster 48
Context Clues
(Meanings may vary. Sample responses are provided.)
1. feigns
   Meaning: pretends
2. ominous
   Meaning: indicating bad things to come
3. incontestable
   Meaning: undeniable
4. prevail
   Meaning: succeed
5. oppressors
   Meaning: those who keep others down by the cruel use of power

Copymaster 49
Context Clues
(Meanings may vary but should be similar to the following.)
1. to begin again
2. destroyed completely
3. diminishes gradually
4. exaggerating the importance of something
5. take advantage of a good situation
6. study something carefully
7. began (used for disasters, such as wars and epidemics)

Copymaster 50
Using Context to Determine Meaning
Word/Meaning
1. seared/burned
2. degenerate/descend; decline
3. inextricably/in a way impossible to untangle; unavoidably
4. confer/bestow; give
5. amnesty/a general pardon

Copymaster 51
Word Origins
1. militancy
   Definition: aggressiveness in pursuing a goal
   Root: from Latin *militare,* to serve as a soldier
2. brutality
   Definition: the state or quality of harshness and cruelty
   Root: from Old French *brut,* rough
3. prodigious
   Definition: impressively great in size, force, or extent
   Root: from Latin *prodigium,* prophetic sign; marvel
4. sustain
   Definition: to keep in existence, maintain
   Root: from Latin *sustinere,* to hold up
5. exhilaration
   Definition: the state of being invigorated or stimulated
   Root: from Greek *hilaros,* cheerful, happy

Copymaster 52
Using a Dictionary
1. prestigious
2. fortitude
3. futile
4. oratory
5. adamant

Copymaster 53
Using Context to Determine Meaning
(Meanings may vary. Sample responses are provided.)
1. in lieu: in place of
2. custody: held under guard
3. warrant: legal document authorizing an officer to make an arrest
4. prosecution: lawyers who represent the government
5. peers: equals

Copymaster 54
Figurative Language
(Definitions may vary. Sample responses are provided.)
1. prow: the forward part of a ship's hull
2. obstinate: stubborn
3. pallid: having an abnormally pale or wan complexion
4. dissonance: a harsh or disagreeable combination of sounds
5. deluge: flood

Copymaster 55
Analogies
1. A; chaos
2. A; discord
3. S; snare
4. A; frailty
5. S; escalate
6. S; insurrection
7. A; comprehensible
8. S; incivility
9. S; incision
10. A; treacherous

Copymaster 56
Context Clues
(Meanings may vary. Sample responses are provided.)
1. watch: post or period of duty of a guard, sentinel, or watchman
2. shadowed: followed after, especially in secret
3. pulse: perceptible emotions or sentiments of a group of people
4. ministered: attended to the wants and needs of others
5. intelligence: secret information, especially, such information about an enemy

Copymaster 57
Prefixes
1. intervene
   Word meaning: to come, appear, or lie between two things
   Prefix and meaning: *inter-,* between
2. perimeter
   Word meaning: a closed curve bounding a plane area
   Prefix and meaning: *peri-,* around
3. transmit
   Word meaning: to send from one person, thing, or place to another
   Prefix and meaning: *trans-,* across
4. atypical
   Word meaning: not typical
   Prefix and meaning: *a-,* not
5. antecedent
   Word meaning: going before
   Prefix and meaning: *ante-,* before

Copymaster 58
Context Clues
(Meanings may vary. Sample responses are provided.)
1. theater: large geographical area in which military operations are coordinated
2. repellent: inspiring aversion or distaste; repulsive
3. profile: biographical essay
4. panel: group of people gathered to plan or to discuss an issue
5. fringe: members of a group holding extreme views

Copymaster 59
Using a Dictionary to Determine Precise Meanings
(Definitions may vary. Sample responses are provided.)
1. concentrated: brought into one main body
2. constitution: person's prevailing state of health
3. neighborhood: approximate amount or range
4. partial: favoring one person or side over another; biased; prejudiced

5. negatives: film, plates, or other photographic materials containing images in which the light areas of the objects rendered appear dark and the dark areas appear light

Copymaster 60
Context Clues
(Meanings may vary. Sample responses are provided.)
1. evoked: called to mind
2. illustrious: renowned, famous
3. invincible: unconquerable, unable to be defeated
4. indignity: something that insults or hurts one's dignity or pride
5. waned: approached an end

Copymaster 61
Synonyms
1. restricted
2. outlasted
3. misfortune
4. inciting
5. impairs

Copymaster 62
Context Clues
(Students' definitions will vary. Sample responses are provided.)
1. chronic
   Context clue: temporary
   Definition: marked by frequent recurrence or long duration
2. fallow
   Context clue: productive
   Definition: dormant
3. exasperated
   Context clue: remain patient
   Definition: aggravated, irritated
4. shrieked
   Context clue: talked quietly
   Definition: cried out in a shrill manner
5. wrenched
   Context clue: wrenched from the wall
   Definition: moved with a violent twist
6. lingered
   Context clue: left quickly
   Definition: tarried
7. descended
   Context clue: rose in the air
   Definition: passed from a higher place to a low one
8. extravagant
   Context clue: very simple
   Definition: ornate or showy, lavish

Copymaster 63
Figurative Language
(Responses may vary but should resemble the following.)
1. Laughter is compared to a ringing bell.
2. Keeping a secret is compared to a Herculean task.
3. Success is compared to a pot of gold.
4. Promise is compared to leaves.
5. The air is being compared to a bone.

6. The full moon is compared to a silver plate.
7. The doll is compared to a fallen vase of red flowers.
8. The leaf is compared to a kite.
9. The rain is compared to ropes.

Copymaster 64
Denotation and Connotation
(Synonyms and descriptions will vary. Sample responses are provided.)
1. failure
   Flop has a more negative and extreme connotation than *failure*, which can mean merely a lack of success.
2. rascal
   A *scamp* is impish and playful while *rascal* has a more negative connotation; a rascal may be not only mischievous but also dishonest.
3. problem
   The connotation of *snag* suggests informality and implies a minor difficulty, while *problem* implies a difficulty that is serious and important.
4. beautiful
   Nice suggests something milder and less strongly appealing than does the more extreme and positive word *beautiful*.
5. spun
   Swirled has a connotation that suggests dance or musical movement while spun implies more prosaic movement.

Copymaster 65
Synonyms
(Student meanings will vary. Sample responses are provided.)
1. amplified
   Context clue: boost; sound of the band; annoyed all the neighbors
   Meaning: enlarged or extended
2. conscious
   Context clue: aware
   Meaning: aware, responsive
3. protruded
   Context clue: jutting out
   Meaning: stuck out
4. efficient
   Context clue: effective
   Meaning: effective, effectual
5. gaunt
   Context clue: scrawny
   Meaning: emaciated, lean
6. enthralled
   Context clue: fascinated
   Meaning: spellbound, captivated
7. aridity
   Context clue: summer drought
   Meaning: dryness, without water
8. innocuous
   Context clue: harmless
   Meaning: inoffensive, safe

Copymaster 66
Analogies
1. a
2. b
3. b
4. a
5. d
6. b
7. b
8. b
9. c
10. b

Copymaster 67
Context Clues
(Students' meanings will vary. Sample responses are provided.)
1. installments
   Meaning: parts
2. baffled
   Meaning: confused
3. trepidation
   Meaning: fear
4. conglomerate
   Meaning: large corporation
5. contaminated
   Meaning: impure
6. swindled
   Meaning: cheated
7. cascaded
   Meaning: fell in a diffused way
8. antagonistic
   Meaning: unfriendly

Copymaster 68
Using Reference Materials
(Students' definitions will vary. Sample dictionary definitions are provided.)
1. cursory
   Dictionary definition: careless
2. dilapidated
   Dictionary definition: rundown; falling to pieces or disrepair
3. reciprocal
   Dictionary definition: mutual
4. bellicose
   Dictionary definition: aggressive; of a quarrelsome or hostile nature
5. diffident
   Dictionary definition: shy; timid

Copymaster 69
Idioms
(Definitions of idioms will vary. Sample responses are provided.)
1. Idiom: hit the sack
   Meaning: went to bed
2. Idiom: blew a fuse
   Meaning: became very angry
3. Idiom: blew the whistle
   Meaning: reported to the authorities
4. Idiom: hold a candle
   Meaning: does not equal in quality
5. Idiom: come clean
   Meaning: confess
6. Idiom: pull the wool over the eyes
   Meaning: fool; trick
7. Idiom: threw in the towel
   Meaning: gave up
8. Idiom: turned over a new leaf
   Meaning: changed, made a new start

Copymaster 70
The Connotative Power of Words
(Synonyms will vary. Possible answers—with synonyms underlined—are provided.)
1. spunky
   The plucky child refused to be frightened by the neighborhood bully.
2. beautiful
   The flower was so lovely that the woman couldn't bear to pick it.
3. gaudy
   The garish costume drew a great deal of attention at the party.
4. angry
   The customer was furious when he discovered that his car couldn't be fixed.
5. approval
   The candidate had worked hard to earn the favor of the voters.

Copymaster 71
Context Clues
(Meanings will vary. Sample responses are provided.)
1. embellished
   Meaning: enhanced
   Context clues: with additional details
2. fabricated
   Meaning: invented
   Context clues: lying to hide his part in the robbery
3. scribbled
   Meaning: wrote carelessly so no one could read his signature
   Context clues: no one could read his signature
4. collision
   Meaning: impact, crash
   Context clues: crushed, with the fire hydrant
5. azure
   Meaning: blue
   Context clues: perfectly blue
6. vial
   Meaning: container
   Context clues: medicine, small glass
7. inferno
   Meaning: a large, hot, destructive blaze
   Context clues: blazing, destroyed the house
8. hindered
   Meaning: held up
   Context clues: icy roads, travelers, delays in their trip

Copymaster 72
Idioms
(Definitions of idioms will vary. Sample responses are provided.)
1. Idiom: put on airs
   Meaning: acted overly important
2. Idiom: made the headlines
   Meaning: reported as a major story in the newspaper
3. Idiom: eat humble pie
   Meaning: admit his mistake with embarrassment
4. Idiom: hit the books
   Meaning: studied hard
5. Idiom: put her foot down
   Meaning: made a firm demand
6. Idiom: eye to eye
   Meaning: agree
7. Idiom: turned a deaf ear
   Meaning: refused to listen
8. Idiom: made the grade
   Meaning: met the requirements

Copymaster 73
Context Clues
(Sentences may vary. Sample responses are provided.)
1. boisterous
   Context clues: so much noise
   Sentence: The kindergarten class was well-behaved, although a bit boisterous.
2. resented
   Context clues: all the attention Tim received
   Sentence: She resented the way the way the politician dismissed her concerns.
3. monologue
   Context clues: alone on the stage, delivered
   Sentence: He became bored when his friend launched into a long monologue on the subject.
4. intimate
   Context clues: diary, her . . . thoughts
   Sentence: It was hard to believe that her most intimate friend had once been a stranger.
5. succinctness
   Context clues: just a few lines
   Sentence: The teacher gave the student a C on the essay because it lacked succinctness.
6. articulate
   Context clues: tried to describe what happened, but he couldn't
   Sentence: His classmates could not understand what he meant, because he couldn't articulate the problem.

Copymaster 74
Antonyms
(Students' meanings will vary. Sample responses are provided.)
1. absurd
   Meaning: ridiculously unreasonable
   Antonym: logical

2. fathom
   Meaning: understand
   Antonym: misinterpret
3. foreboding
   Meaning: prediction
   Antonym: conclusion
4. hospitable
   Meaning: cordial
   Antonym: rude
5. impersonally
   Meaning: impartially, neutrally
   Antonym: friendly
6. languorous
   Meaning: weary
   Antonym: energetic
7. lull
   Meaning: temporary calm
   Antonym: continuation
8. resolutely
   Meaning: with determination
   Antonym: accidentally
9. slacken
   Meaning: become less active
   Antonym: increase
10. suitor
    Meaning: one who courts a woman
    Antonym: enemy

Copymaster 75
Synonyms
(Responses will vary. Sample responses are provided.)
1. instructed
   Synonym: ordered
   Change in meaning: makes the instruction more serious
2. fib
   Synonym: lie
   Change in meaning: makes the untruth seem more serious
3. unattractive
   Synonym: ugly
   Change in meaning: worsens the city's appearance
4. stain
   Synonym: discolor
   Change in meaning: lessens the fabric damage
5. slid
   Synonym: skidded
   Change in meaning: makes the action more serious
6. lingered
   Synonym: loitered
   Change in meaning: makes the waiting around more aimless
7. waiting
   Synonym: procrastinating
   Change in meaning: makes the delay seem more intentional
8. vigilant
   Synonym: careful
   Change in meaning: lessens the degree of close attention

Copymaster 76
Context Clues

(Sample responses are provided.)
1. aurally
   Context clue: hearing the information
2. castigation
   Context clue: harsh verbal scolding
3. egotistical
   Context clue: extreme conceit
4. enigmatic
   Context clue: puzzling to figure out
5. intimation
   Context clue: a hint
6. indispensable
   Context clue: absolutely essential
7. skewed
   Context clue: misrepresentation of the facts
8. facetious
   Context clue: humorous
9. ungainly
   Context clue: lacks grace
10. cataclysmic
    Context clue: overwhelmingly destructive

Copymaster 77
Context Clues

(Students' sentences will vary. Sample responses are provided.)
1. cacophony
   Context clue: chaotic sound
   Sentence: When the tree crashed to earth, the forest animals filled the air with a cacophony of roars and snorts.
2. calloused
   Context clue: cruel and insensitive
   His calloused shrug told her all she needed to know about his unwillingness to help.
3. matriculation
   Context clue: enrollment and registration
   Sentence: She delayed her matriculation into business school by one year so that she could earn money to help pay for tuition.
4. prodigal
   Context clue: extreme generosity
   Sentence: The millionaire was so prodigal with his expenditures that he had to raise some money by selling one of his cars.
5. mendacious
   Context clue: false
   Sentence: As she looked into his eyes, the teacher could tell that the boy's denial was mendacious.

Copymaster 78
Word Origins

(Student responses may vary. Sample responses are provided.)
Word/Origin and Meaning/Relationship Between Origin and Present Meaning
1. cavalcade/*caballus*, horse/a procession of riders

2. eulogy/*eulogia*, to praise/a speech of praise
3. energy/*energeia*, activity/capacity for doing a lot of activity
4. affluent/*affluere*, to flow abundantly/an abundance of wealth or goods
5. simulate/*simulare*, to copy/to copy under the same conditions

Copymaster 79
Context Clues

(Definitions may vary. Sample responses are provided.)
1. credence
   Context clue: distrust
   Definition: acceptance as true
   Sentence: Because he had a sterling reputation for honesty, we all put credence in Jake's report that he spotted a bear near Main Street.
2. sociable
   Context clue: shy
   Definition: friendly
   Sentence: Dan was so sociable that he was usually the last one to leave a party.
3. intrepid
   Context clue: cowardly
   Definition: brave
   Sentence: The intrepid climber did not allow the icy surface to affect his goal of reaching the mountain peak before dusk.
4. indefatigable
   Context clue: lacked energy
   Definition: untiring
   Sentence: The campaign assistant was an indefatigable worker who was on the job at least 12 hours a day.
5. cogent
   Context clue: confusing
   Definition: organized
   Sentence: The doctor's cogent analysis of her medical condition persuaded my mother to seek treatment for her discomfort.

Copymaster 80
Denotation and Connotation

(Explanations for choices will vary. Sample responses are provided.)
1. dynamic
   Dynamic suggests being active and inspirational, both qualities of an effective speaker.
2. vigorous
   Vigorous is the best choice because it suggests good health.
3. soundless
   Soundless suggests the presence of movement that has no sound, *still* implies the lack of movement, and *quiet* has no particular connotation either way.
4. dining
   Dining suggests more elegance than *eating,* and much more more style than *chowing down.*
5. convincing
   While both *valid* and *sound* suggest logical, flawless arguments, *convincing* implies an argument that overcomes objections.

Copymaster 81
Suffixes
Word/Base and Meaning/Suffix and Meaning/Definition
1. languorous/languor; dreaminess/-ous; full of/listless
2. foreboding/forebode; foretell/-ing; action or process/ an omen
3. resolutely/resolute; bold/-ly; manner/courageously
4. abashed/abash; to astonish/-ed; past tense/ashamed
5. dryness/dry; without water/-ness; condition/condition of being without water
6. dispenser/dispense; to deal out/-er; one that performs an action/vending device
7. grievous/grieve; to suffer/-ous; full of/serious
8. spacious/space; area/-ous; full of/expansive
9. cellular/cell; small unit/-ular; pertaining to/with cells
10. alphabetize/alphabet; letters in a set order/-ize; engage in activity/to sort letters in alphabetical order

Copymaster 82
Context Clues
1. abyss
   Context clue: a huge crevice
2. perambulator
   Context clue: in England, baby carriages
3. egregious
   Context clue: horrible
4. glib
   Context clue: smooth
5. Francophile
   Context clue: obsessed with all things French
6. metronome
   Context clue: swinging pendulum that keeps time
7. autonomous
   Context clue: make certain decisions independently
8. adroit
   Context clue: skillful
9. altruistic
   Context clue: put other's needs above their own
10. capriole
    Context clue: this complex jump

Copymaster 83
Analogies
1. b. shriek
2. c. sorority
3. b. Rome
4. c. five hundred
5. a. hand
6. c. crumb
7. a. Model-T
8. b. rein
9. c. disapprove
10. c. drenched

Copymaster 84
The Connotative Power of Words
(Answers may vary. Sample responses are provided.)

an accepting   deviation
1. Taos is a tolerant village, well accustomed to whimsy.
2. It has been said that if the late James Thurber had been raised here he
   publicized   behaviors
   would never have celebrated the antics of his family in print, since what
   weird
   seems outlandish in Columbus, Ohio, seems fairly normal in Taos.
   originality
3. In Taos a certain amount of eccentricity is required for conformity.
   fitting in   onlookers
4. Interest among the spectators quickened, however, when some of them saw—or thought they saw—a pistol in the hand of the pseudo-woman.
   fake
   fast   walked quickly
5. The fleet-footed ones, who had beaten the rush to the tellers' windows and
   told
   therefore left early, spread the news of this unusual sight around Taos Plaza.

Copymaster 85
Context Clues
(Students' definitions may vary. Sample responses are provided.)
1. pessimist
   Context clue: searched for the good in everything
   Contrast; Definition: one who finds fault in everything
2. voluminous
   Context clue: scanty
   Contrast; Definition: extensive
3. euphonious
   Context clue: pleasing to the ear
   Comparison; Definition: pleasant sounding
4. cliches
   Context clue: imaginative words and phrases
   Contrast; Definition: tired, overused words and phrases
5. complacent
   Context clue: wild
   Contrast; Definition: calm

Copymaster 86
Context Clues
(Students' definitions and sentences may vary. Sample responses are provided.)
1. hippophobia
   Context clue: horse, crying from fear
   Definition: fear of horses
   Sentence: The rancher's hippophobia prevented him from overseeing his land on horseback.
2. matriarchal
   Context clue: women control
   Definition: run by women
   Sentence: As Ian sat in the room with his mother, his

grandmother, and his aunts, he realized how matriarchal his family was.
3. indifferent
Context clue: hold his hand over his mouth
Definition: aloof, detached
Sentence: While his mother applauded enthusiastically, his brother appeared indifferent about Tony's stupendous catch.
4. somniferous
Context clue: used during naptime, actually fell asleep
Definition: sleep inducing
Sentence: The somniferous sound of the fog horn put the entire family to sleep early.
5. tacit
Context clue: nod, approval
Definition: implied but not actually expressed
Sentence: Josh concluded that her smile indicated tacit approval of his new shirt.

Copymaster 87
Analogies
1. beguiling
2. snare
3. vile
4. stealthy
5. succumb
6. entice
7. disconsolate
8. contender
9. chide
10. amused

Copymaster 88
Antonyms
(Answers will vary. Sample responses are provided.)
1. formidable
Antonym: unimpressive, weak
2. ponderous
Antonym: graceful, light, lively
3. construct
Antonym: destroy, demolish, raze
4. fidelity
Antonym: treachery, faithlessness
5. uncommunicative
Antonym: talkative, garrulous
6. innovative
Antonym: old-fashioned, familiar, dated
7. entice
Antonym: revolt, repel, disgust
8. disconsolate
Antonym: joyous, cheerful, merry
9. unite
Antonym: sunder, fracture, split
10. chaos
Antonym: order, organization, tranquility, peace
11. dwindle
Antonym: increase, grow, multiply
12. peril
Antonym: safety, security, refuge
13. travail
Antonym: ease, peace, comfort
14. dire
Antonym: delightful, enjoyable
15. anguish
Antonym: joy, peace, relief, comfort

Copymaster 89
Context Clues
(Answers will vary. Sample responses are provided.)
1. Context: whisked away his great stone door
Meaning of *cap*: to put a cover over
Meaning in context: "To put a cover over a quiver," a container for arrows, makes sense in context.
2. Context: The Cyclops is a one-eyed giant; deep
Meaning of *crater*: depression or hole in a volcano
Meaning in context: "The giant eye of the Cyclops looked like a hole in a volcano" makes sense in context.
3. Context: small, pitiful
Meaning of *twiggy*: like a twig—a small, slender stick or branch of a tree
Meaning in context: "Pitiful, small, and slender or fragile" makes sense in context.

Copymaster 90
Latin Roots
(Answers will vary according to sources used. Sample responses are provided.)
1. adversary
Etymology: from the Latin *adversarius,* enemy, from *adversus,* "against"
Explanation: The word means an opponent, someone "against" a person.
2. appall
Etymology: from Old French *apalir: a-,* "to" (from Latin *ad-*), + *palir,* "to grow pale," from Latin *pallere* (also "to grow pale")
Explanation: Someone who is *appalled* (filled with shock or dismay) is likely to "grow pale."
3. quest
Etymology: from the Latin *questa,* from *quaerere,* "to seek"
Explanation: To *quest* means "to journey in search of (seeking) something."
4. desolate
Etymology: from Latin *desolatus,* from *desolare,* "to abandon," from *de-* (intensive) + *solus,* "alone"
Explanation: *Desolate* means "empty" or "alone."
5. contempt
Etymology: from Latin *contemptus,* from *contemnere,* "to despise"
Explanation: *Contempt* is disdain or scorn—the attitude of despising something.
6. formidable
Etymology: Old French from Latin *formidabilis,* from *formidare,* "to fear," from *formido,* "fear"
Explanation: Something *formidable* often inspires fear.

Copymaster 91
Using Synonyms
(Choices of synonyms may vary. Sample responses are provided.)
1. indecisiveness
   Synonym: dithering
2. emptiness
   Synonym: desolation
3. reckless
   Synonym: rash
4. struggle
   Synonym: conflict
5. brashness
   Synonym: gall
6. explanation
   Synonym: justification
7. showered
   Synonym: lavished
8. chaos
   Synonym: turmoil
9. detestable
   Synonym: contemptible
10. repayment
    Synonym: restitution

Copymaster 92
Context Clues
(Answers may vary. Sample responses are provided.)
1. bepaint
   Meaning: color or stain
   Context clues: blush, cheeks, hidden by night
2. attending
   Meaning: listening
   Context clues: "Ears" would listen to "tongues" (speech) and "music."
3. devise
   Meaning: imagine, understand
   Context clues: Romeo is saying he never hurt Mercutio, but loves him, though Mercutio believes otherwise.
4. worms' meat
   Meaning: a corpse
   Context clues: Worms are decomposers; Mercutio will die of his wounds.

Copymaster 93
Using Reference Materials
(Meanings will vary according to sources used. Sample responses are provided.)
1. beseeming
   Meaning: appropriate for; befitting
2. cankered
   Meaning: corrupt, infected
3. covert
   Meaning: underbrush
4. baleful
   Meaning: harmful
5. couch
   Meaning: to lie down for rest

6. wooed
   Meaning: sought the affection of with intent to marry
7. rote
   Meaning: memorization
8. driveling
   Meaning: foolish
9. troth
   Meaning: good faith, fidelity, pledge
10. trow
    Meaning: to think

Copymaster 94
Word Origins
(Answers will vary according to sources used. Sample responses are provided.)
1. tomorrow
   Origin: Anglo-Saxon *to morgenne,* "in the morning"
2. audience
   Origin: Latin *audientia,* from *audiens,* from *audire,* "to hear"
3. heaven
   Origin: Anglo-Saxon *heofan*
4. prologue
   Origin: Greek *prologos: pro-,* before, + *legein,* "to speak"
5. pity
   Origin: Latin *pietas,* from *pius,* "dutiful"
6. woe
   Origin: Anglo-Saxon *wa,* "woe!"
7. dear
   Origin: Anglo-Saxon *deore*
8. quarrel
   Origin: Latin *querela,* from *queri,* "to complain"
9. meddle
   Origin: Old French *medler,* from *mesler,* from Latin *miscere,* "to mix"
10. slander
    Origin: Greek *scandalon,* "trap"

Copymaster 95
Using a Glossary
1. humor
   Meaning: whim, fancy
2. fair
   Meaning: courteous
3. strange
   Meaning: reserved
4. sweet
   Meaning: delightful
5 suffer
   Meaning: bear with patience, or allow (see *sufferance)*
6. wreak
   Meaning: revenge
7. abused
   Meaning: disfigured
8. copest
   Meaning: matches (*copest with)*
9. cross
   Meaning: perverse ("in opposition to what is good or right")

Copymaster 96
Expanding Vocabulary
(Meanings and sentences will vary. Sample responses are provided.)

1. reigned
   Meaning: to be predominant or prevalent
   Sentence: Chaos reigned at the scene of the accident.

2. bid
   Meaning: to order, command
   Sentence: Imperiously, he bid the others to move out of his way.

3. yonder
   Meaning: being at an indicated distance, usually within sight
   Sentence: Meet me yonder, under that billboard.

4. morsel
   Meaning: a small piece or amount, especially of food, often tasty
   Sentence: The children consumed every last morsel of lunch.

5. sunder
   Meaning: to break into parts; sever
   Sentence: Rocks in the rapids threatened to sunder the raft.

6. inauspicious
   Meaning: unfavorable
   Sentence: The inauspicious forecast caused us to postpone our plans.

7. To ensign
   Meaning: an emblem or sign
   Sentence: In many places, robins are ensigns of spring.